GLENCOE MATHEMATICS

D1296121

Algebra 1

Chapter 10
Resource Masters

Glencoe
McGraw-Hill

New York, New York
Columbus, Ohio
Chicago, Illinois
Peoria, Illinois
Woodland Hills, California

Consumable Workbooks

Many of the worksheets contained in the Chapter Resource Masters booklets are available as consumable workbooks in both English and Spanish.

Study Guide and Intervention Workbook	0-07-827753-1
Study Guide and Intervention Workbook (Spanish)	0-07-827754-X
Skills Practice Workbook	0-07-827747-7
Skills Practice Workbook (Spanish)	0-07-827749-3
Practice Workbook	0-07-827748-5
Practice Workbook (Spanish)	0-07-827750-7

ANSWERS FOR WORKBOOKS The answers for Chapter 10 of these workbooks can be found in the back of this Chapter Resource Masters booklet.

Glencoe/McGraw-Hill

A Division of The McGraw-Hill Companies

Send all inquiries to:
The McGraw-Hill Companies
8787 Orion Place
Columbus, OH 43240-4027

ISBN: 0-07-827734-5

Algebra 1
Chapter 10 Resource Masters

2 3 4 5 6 7 8 9 10 024 11 10 09 08 07 06 05 04 03

Contents

Teacher's Guide to Using the Chapter 10 Resource Masters

The ***Fast File*** Chapter Resource system allows you to conveniently file the resources you use most often. The *Chapter 10 Resource Masters* includes the core materials needed for Chapter 10. These materials include worksheets, extensions, and assessment options. The answers for these pages appear at the back of this booklet.

All of the materials found in this booklet are included for viewing and printing in the *Algebra 1 TeacherWorks* CD-ROM.

Vocabulary Builder Pages vii–viii include a student study tool that presents up to twenty of the key vocabulary terms from the chapter. Students are to record definitions and/or examples for each term. You may suggest that students highlight or star the terms with which they are not familiar.

WHEN TO USE Give these pages to students before beginning Lesson 10-1. Encourage them to add these pages to their Algebra Study Notebook. Remind them to add definitions and examples as they complete each lesson.

Study Guide and Intervention
Each lesson in *Algebra 1* addresses two objectives. There is one Study Guide and Intervention master for each objective.

WHEN TO USE Use these masters as reteaching activities for students who need additional reinforcement. These pages can also be used in conjunction with the Student Edition as an instructional tool for students who have been absent.

Skills Practice There is one master for each lesson. These provide computational practice at a basic level.

WHEN TO USE These masters can be used with students who have weaker mathematics backgrounds or need additional reinforcement.

Practice There is one master for each lesson. These problems more closely follow the structure of the Practice and Apply section of the Student Edition exercises. These exercises are of average difficulty.

WHEN TO USE These provide additional practice options or may be used as homework for second day teaching of the lesson.

Reading to Learn Mathematics
One master is included for each lesson. The first section of each master asks questions about the opening paragraph of the lesson in the Student Edition. Additional questions ask students to interpret the context of and relationships among terms in the lesson. Finally, students are asked to summarize what they have learned using various representation techniques.

WHEN TO USE This master can be used as a study tool when presenting the lesson or as an informal reading assessment after presenting the lesson. It is also a helpful tool for ELL (English Language Learner) students.

Enrichment There is one extension master for each lesson. These activities may extend the concepts in the lesson, offer an historical or multicultural look at the concepts, or widen students' perspectives on the mathematics they are learning. These are not written exclusively for honors students, but are accessible for use with all levels of students.

WHEN TO USE These may be used as extra credit, short-term projects, or as activities for days when class periods are shortened.

Assessment Options

The assessment masters in the *Chapter 10 Resources Masters* offer a wide range of assessment tools for intermediate and final assessment. The following lists describe each assessment master and its intended use.

Chapter Assessment

CHAPTER TESTS

- *Form 1* contains multiple-choice questions and is intended for use with basic level students.
- *Forms 2A and 2B* contain multiple-choice questions aimed at the average level student. These tests are similar in format to offer comparable testing situations.
- *Forms 2C and 2D* are composed of free-response questions aimed at the average level student. These tests are similar in format to offer comparable testing situations. Grids with axes are provided for questions assessing graphing skills.
- *Form 3* is an advanced level test with free-response questions. Grids without axes are provided for questions assessing graphing skills.

  All of the above tests include a free-response Bonus question.

- The **Open-Ended Assessment** includes performance assessment tasks that are suitable for all students. A scoring rubric is included for evaluation guidelines. Sample answers are provided for assessment.
- A **Vocabulary Test**, suitable for all students, includes a list of the vocabulary words in the chapter and ten questions assessing students' knowledge of those terms. This can also be used in conjunction with one of the chapter tests or as a review worksheet.

Intermediate Assessment

- Four free-response **quizzes** are included to offer assessment at appropriate intervals in the chapter.
- A **Mid-Chapter Test** provides an option to assess the first half of the chapter. It is composed of both multiple-choice and free-response questions.

Continuing Assessment

- The **Cumulative Review** provides students an opportunity to reinforce and retain skills as they proceed through their study of Algebra 1. It can also be used as a test. This master includes free-response questions.
- The **Standardized Test Practice** offers continuing review of algebra concepts in various formats, which may appear on the standardized tests that they may encounter. This practice includes multiple-choice, grid-in, and quantitative-comparison questions. Bubble-in and grid-in answer sections are provided on the master.

Answers

- Page A1 is an answer sheet for the Standardized Test Practice questions that appear in the Student Edition on pages 580–581. This improves students' familiarity with the answer formats they may encounter in test taking.
- The answers for the lesson-by-lesson masters are provided as reduced pages with answers appearing in red.
- Full-size answer keys are provided for the assessment masters in this booklet.

10 Reading to Learn Mathematics

Vocabulary Builder

his is an alphabetical list of the key vocabulary terms you will learn in Chapter 10. As you study the chapter, complete each term's definition or description. Remember to add the page number where you found the term. Add these pages to your Algebra Study Notebook to review vocabulary at the end of the chapter.

Vocabulary Term	Found on Page	Definition/Description/Example
axis of symmetry SIH·muh·tree		
common ratio		
completing the square		
compound interest		
discriminant		
exponential decay EHK·spuh·NEHN·chuhl		
exponential function		
exponential growth		
geometric means		
geometric sequence		

(continued on the next page)

NAME ______________________________ DATE ____________ PERIOD _____

10 Reading to Learn Mathematics

Vocabulary Builder *(continued)*

Vocabulary Term	Found on Page	Definition/Description/Example
maximum		
minimum		
parabola puh·RA·buh·luh		
quadratic equation kwah·DRA·tihk		
Quadratic Formula		
quadratic function		
roots		
symmetry		
vertex		
zeros		

NAME ______________________________ DATE ____________ PERIOD _____

10-1 Study Guide and Intervention

Graphing Quadratic Functions

Graph Quadratic Functions

Quadratic Function	a function described by an equation of the form $f(x) = ax^2 + bx + c$, where $a \neq 0$	**Example:** $y = 2x^2 + 3x + 8$

The degree of a quadratic function is 2, and the exponents are positive. Graphs of quadratic functions have a general shape called a **parabola**. A parabola opens upward and has a **minimum point** when the value of a is positive, and a parabola opens downward and has a **maximum point** when the value of a is negative.

Example 1 **Use a table of values to graph $y = x^2 - 4x + 1$.**

x	y
−1	6
0	1
1	−2
2	−3
3	−2
4	1

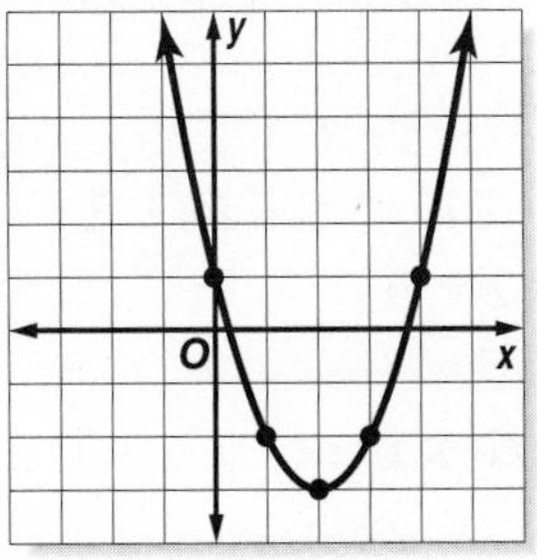

Graph the ordered pairs in the table and connect them with a smooth curve.

Example 2 **Use a table of values to graph $y = -x^2 - 6x - 7$.**

x	y
−6	−7
−5	−2
−4	1
−3	2
−2	1
−1	−2
0	−7

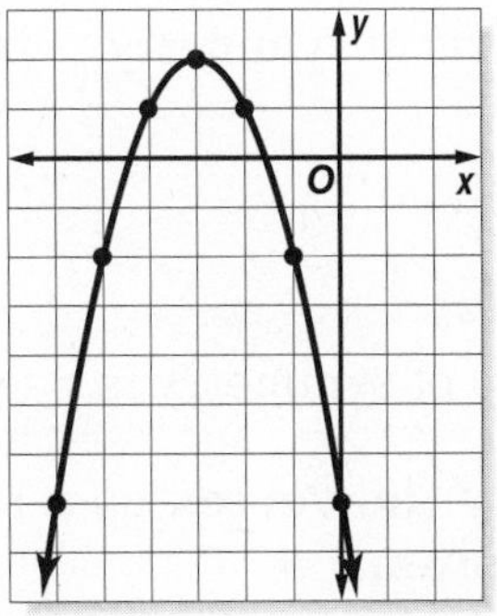

Graph the ordered pairs in the table and connect them with a smooth curve.

Exercises

Use a table of values to graph each function.

1. $y = x^2 + 2$

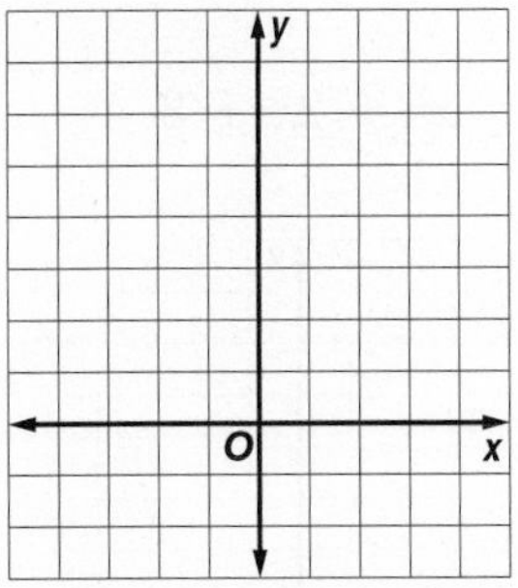

2. $y = -x^2 - 4$

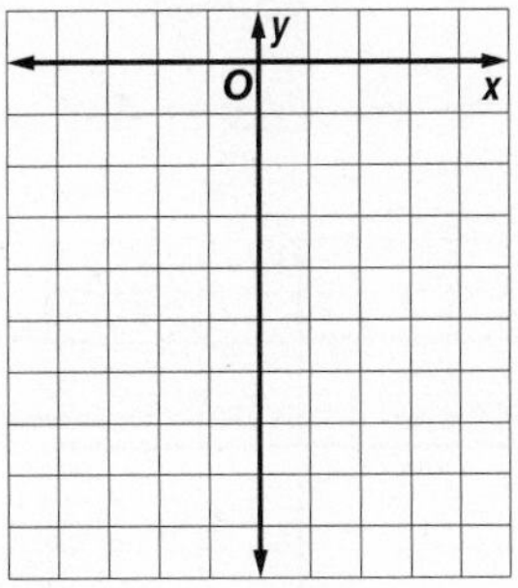

3. $y = x^2 - 3x + 2$

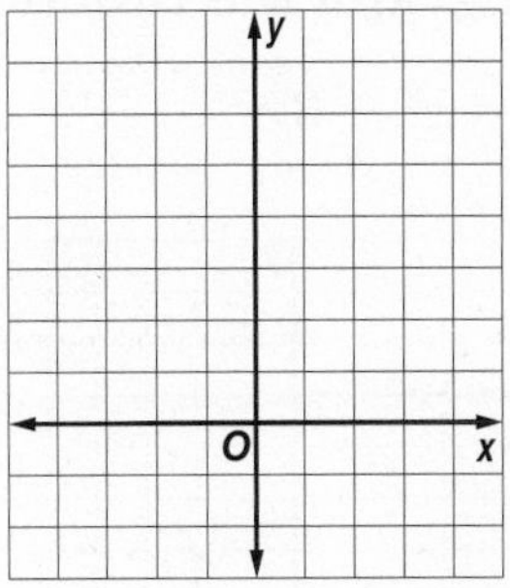

Lesson 10-1

10-1 Study Guide and Intervention *(continued)*

Graphing Quadratic Functions

Symmetry and Vertices Parabolas have a geometric property called **symmetry**. That is, if the figure is folded in half, each half will match the other half exactly. The vertical line containing the fold line is called the **axis of symmetry**.

Axis of Symmetry	For the parabola $y = ax^2 + bx + c$, where $a \neq 0$, the line $x = -\frac{b}{2a}$ is the axis of symmetry.	**Example:** The axis of symmetry of $y = x^2 + 2x + 5$ is the line $x = -1$.

The axis of symmetry contains the minimum or maximum point of the parabola, the **vertex**.

Example **Consider the graph of $y = 2x^2 + 4x + 1$.**

a. Write the equation of the axis of symmetry.

In $y = 2x^2 + 4x + 1$, $a = 2$ and $b = 4$. Substitute these values into the equation of the axis of symmetry.

$$x = -\frac{b}{2a}$$

$$x = -\frac{4}{2(2)} = -1$$

The axis of symmetry is $x = -1$.

b. Find the coordinates of the vertex.

Since the equation of the axis of symmetry is $x = -1$ and the vertex lies on the axis, the x-coordinate of the vertex is -1.

$y = 2x^2 + 4x + 1$ Original equation
$y = 2(-1)^2 + 4(-1) + 1$ Substitute.
$y = 2(1) - 4 + 1$ Simplify.
$y = -1$

The vertex is at $(-1, -1)$.

c. Identify the vertex as a maximum or a minimum.

Since the coefficient of the x^2-term is positive, the parabola opens upward, and the vertex is a minimum point.

d. Graph the function.

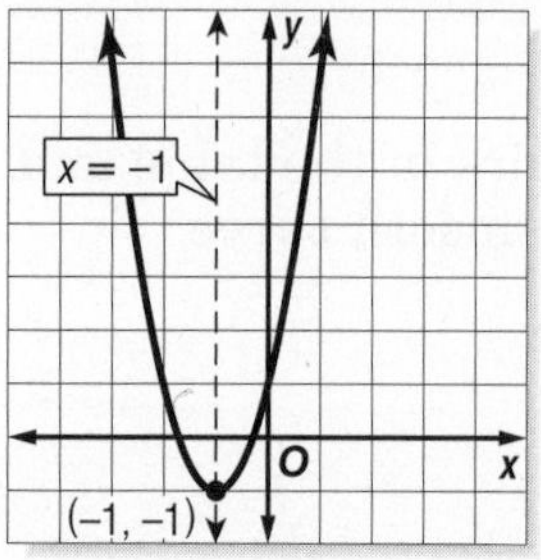

Exercises

Write the equation of the axis of symmetry, and find the coordinates of the vertex of the graph of each function. Identify the vertex as a maximum or a minimum. Then graph the function.

1. $y = x^2 + 3$

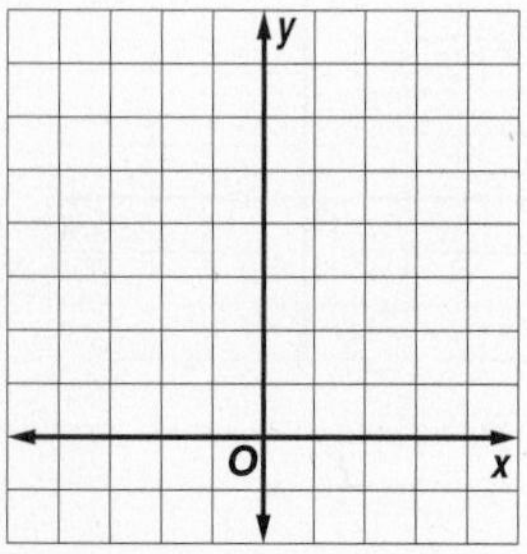

2. $y = -x^2 - 4x - 4$

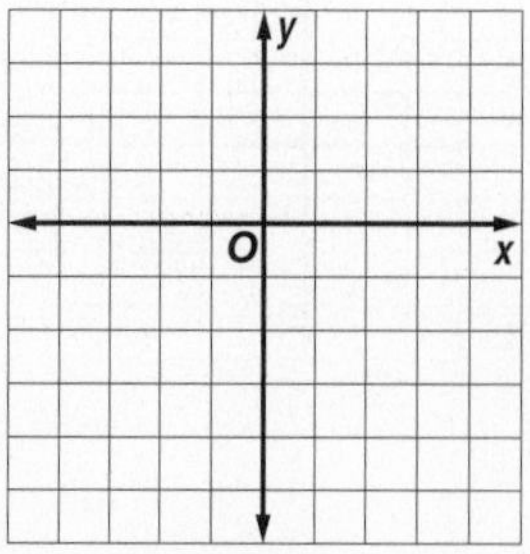

3. $y = x^2 + 2x + 3$

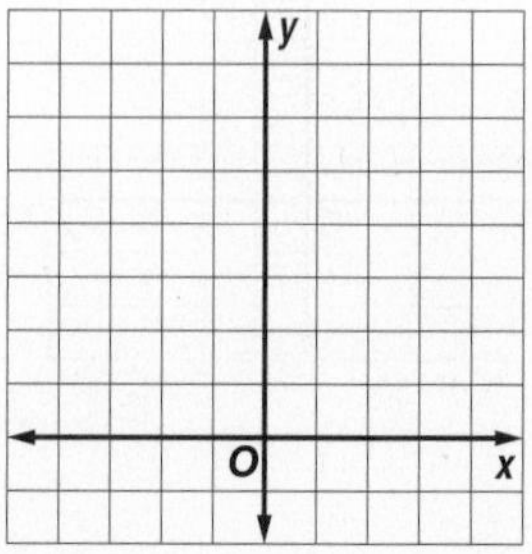

10-1 Skills Practice

Graphing Quadratic Functions

Use a table of values to graph each function.

1. $y = x^2 - 4$

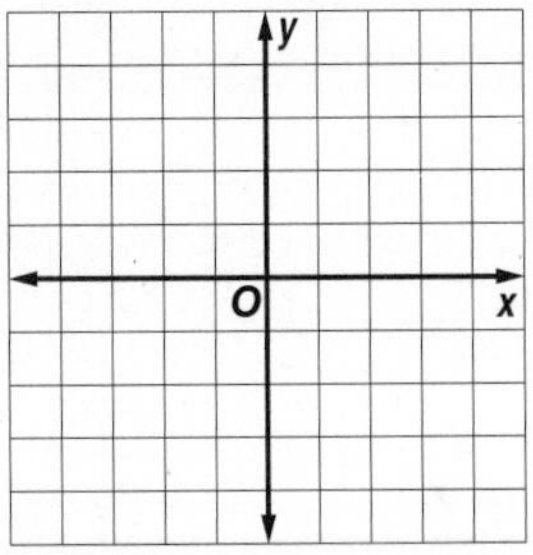

2. $y = -x^2 + 3$

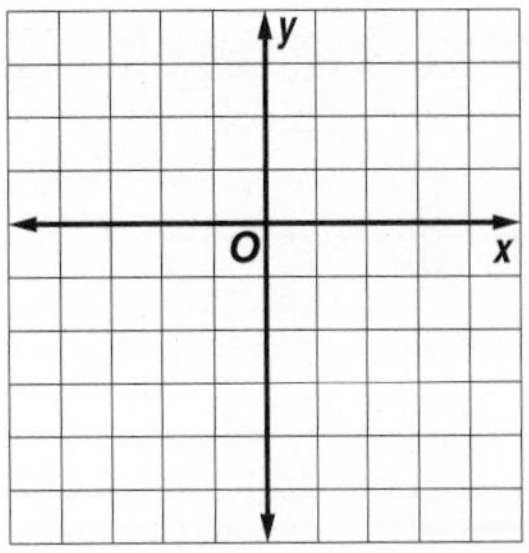

3. $y = x^2 - 2x - 6$

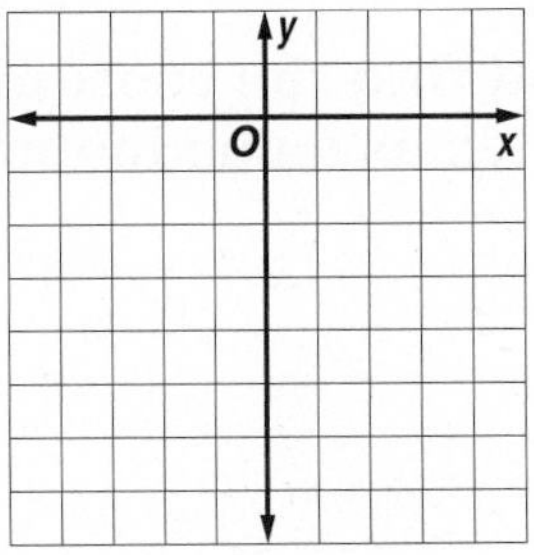

4. $y = -x^2 - 4x + 1$

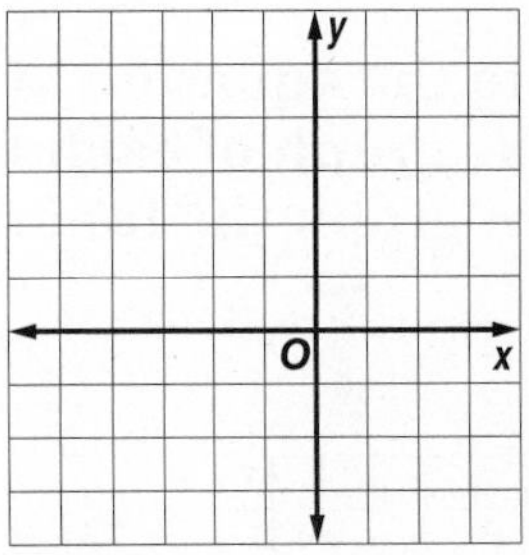

Write the equation of the axis of symmetry, and find the coordinates of the vertex of the graph of each function. Identify the vertex as a maximum or minimum. Then graph the function.

5. $y = 2x^2$

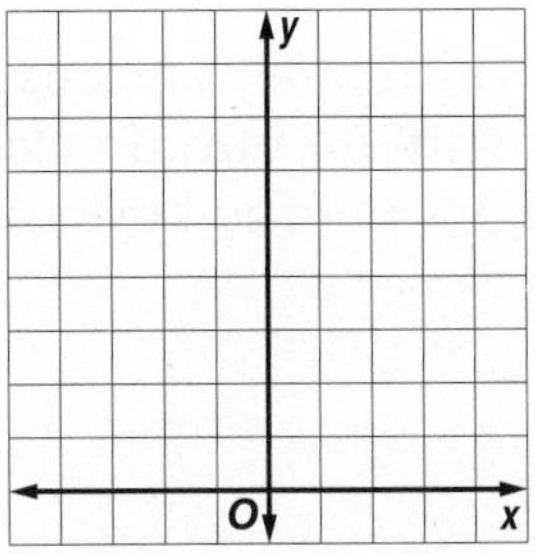

6. $y = x^2 - 2x - 5$

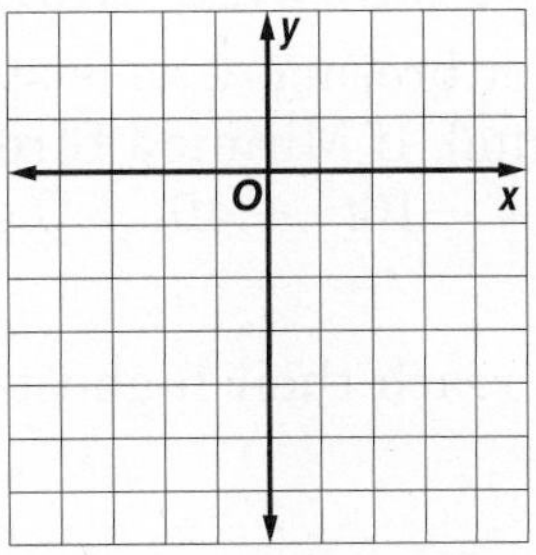

7. $y = -x^2 + 4x - 1$

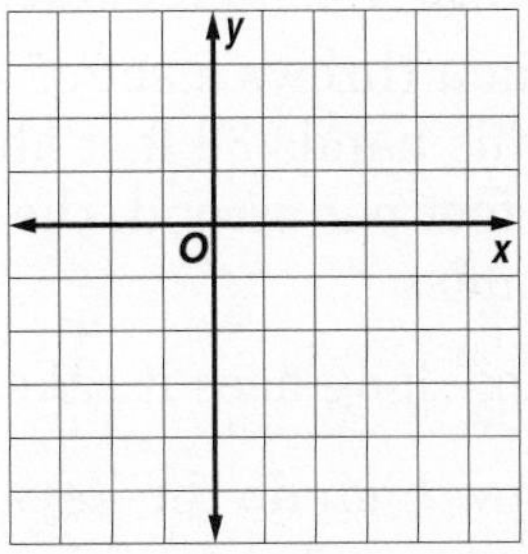

8. $y = -x^2 - 2x + 2$

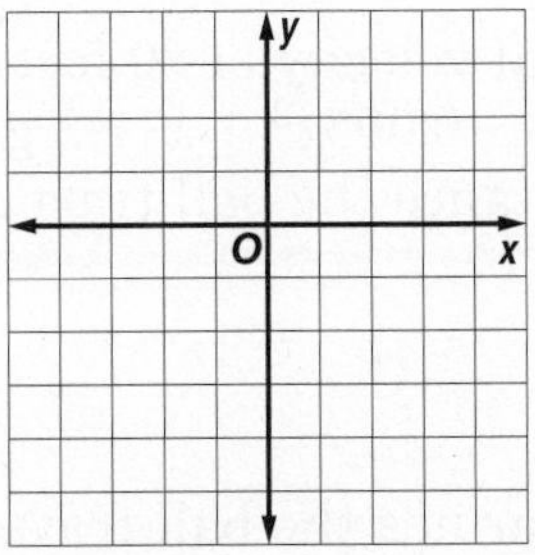

9. $y = 2x^2 + 4x - 2$

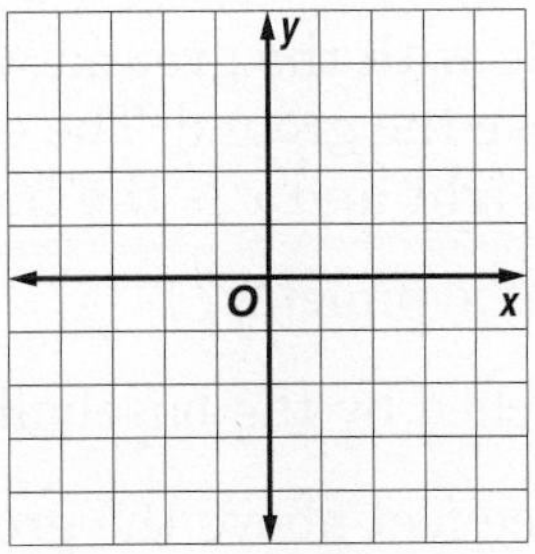

10. $y = -2x^2 - 4x + 6$

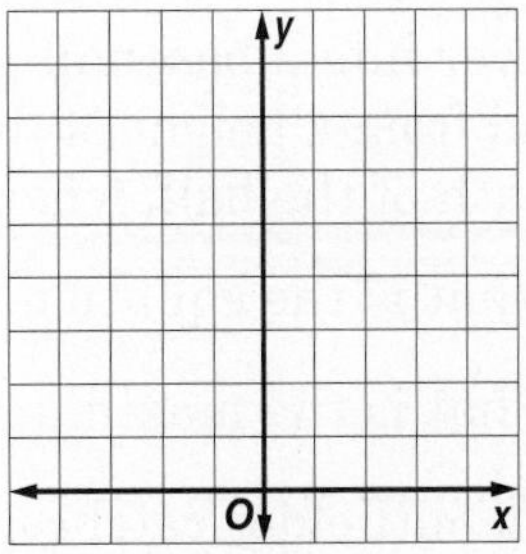

NAME ______________________ DATE __________ PERIOD _____

10-1 Practice

Graphing Quadratic Functions

Use a table of values to graph each function.

1. $y = -x^2 + 2$

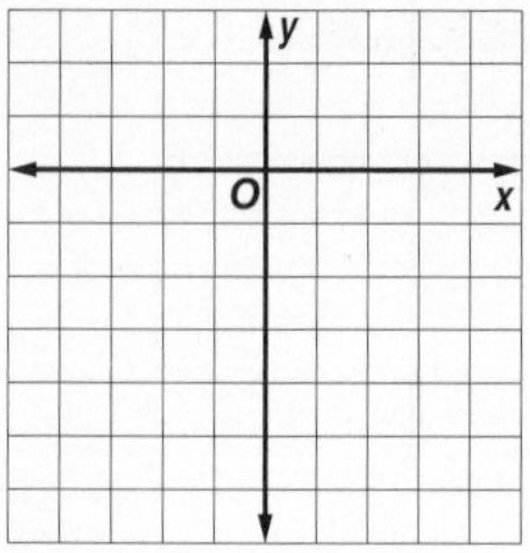

2. $y = x^2 - 6x + 3$

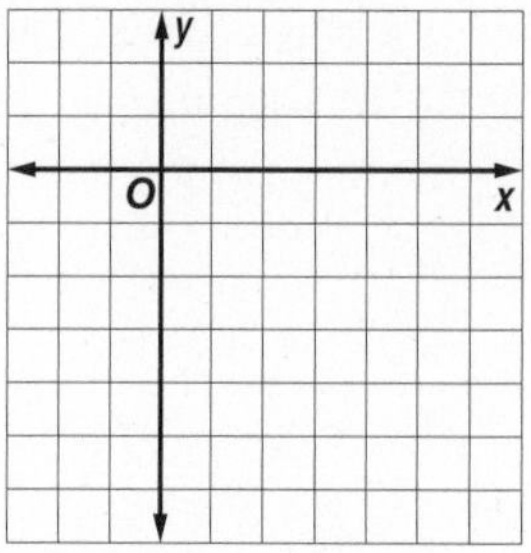

3. $y = -2x^2 - 8x - 5$

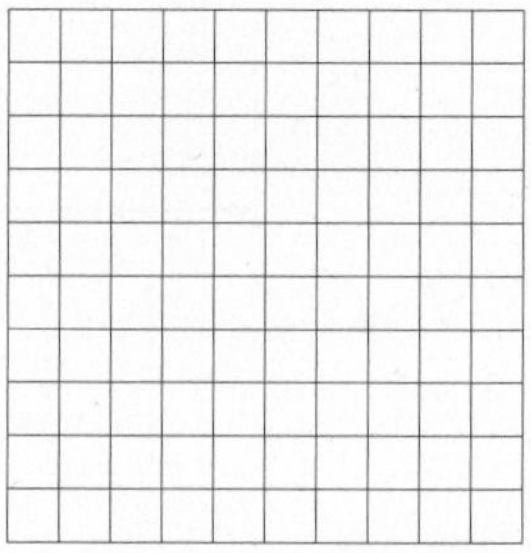

Write the equation of the axis of symmetry, and find the coordinates of the vertex of the graph of each function. Identify the vertex as a maximum or minimum. Then graph the function.

4. $y = -x^2 + 3$

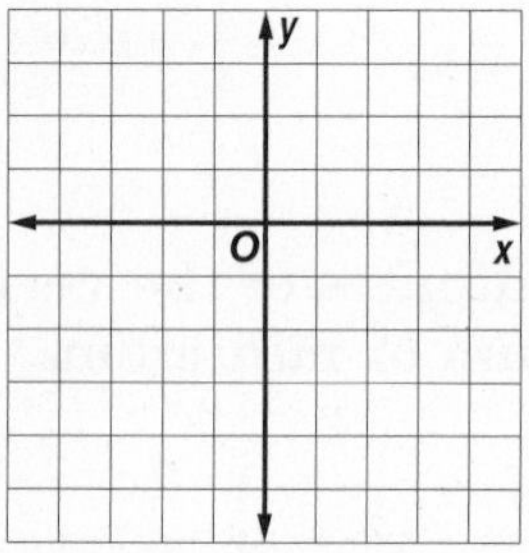

5. $y = -2x^2 + 8x - 3$

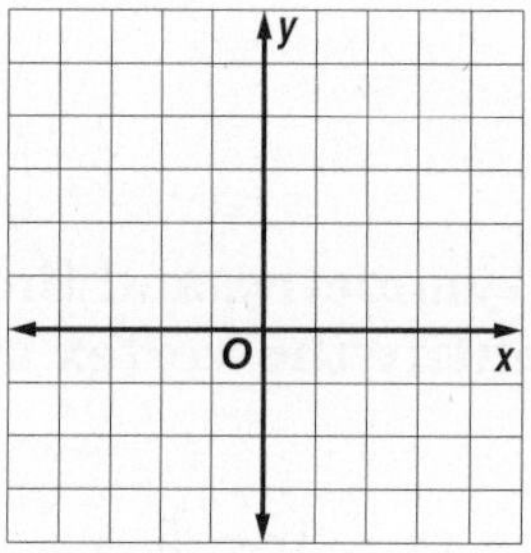

6. $y = 2x^2 + 8x + 1$

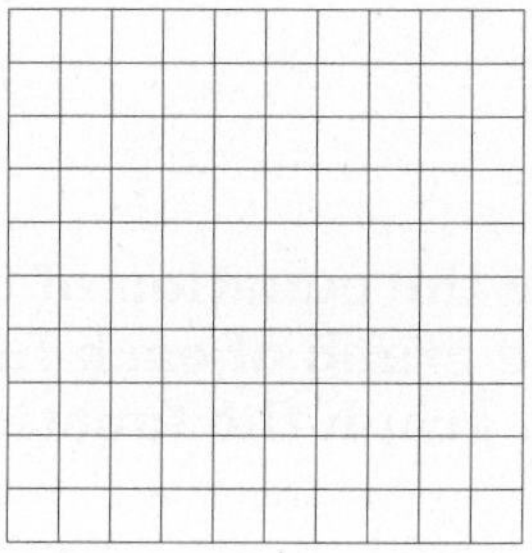

PHYSICS For Exercises 7–9, use the following information.

Miranda throws a set of keys up to her brother, who is standing on a third-story balcony with his hands 38 feet above the ground. If Miranda throws the keys with an initial velocity of 40 feet per second, the equation $h = -16t^2 + 40t + 5$ gives the height h of the keys after t seconds.

7. How long does it take the keys to reach their highest point?

8. How high do the keys reach?

9. Will her brother be able to catch the keys? Explain.

BASEBALL For Exercises 10–12, use the following information.

A player hits a baseball at a 45° angle with the ground with an initial velocity of 80 feet per second from a height of three feet above the ground. The equation $h = -0.005x^2 + x + 3$ gives the path of the ball, where h is the height and x is the horizontal distance the ball travels.

10. What is the equation of the axis of symmetry?

11. What is the maximum height reached by the baseball?

12. An outfielder catches the ball three feet above the ground. How far has the ball traveled horizontally when the outfielder catches it?

10-1 Reading to Learn Mathematics

Graphing Quadratic Functions

Pre-Activity **How can you coordinate a fireworks display with recorded music?**

Read the introduction to Lesson 10-1 at the top of page 524 in your textbook.

According to the graph, at what height does the rocket explode and in how many seconds after being launched?

Reading the Lesson

1. The standard form for a ______________ function is $y = ax^2 + bx + c$. For the function $y = 2x^2 - 5x + 3$, the value of a is ________, the value of b is ________, and the value of c is ________.

2. The graphs of two quadratic functions are shown below. Complete each statement about the graphs.

A.

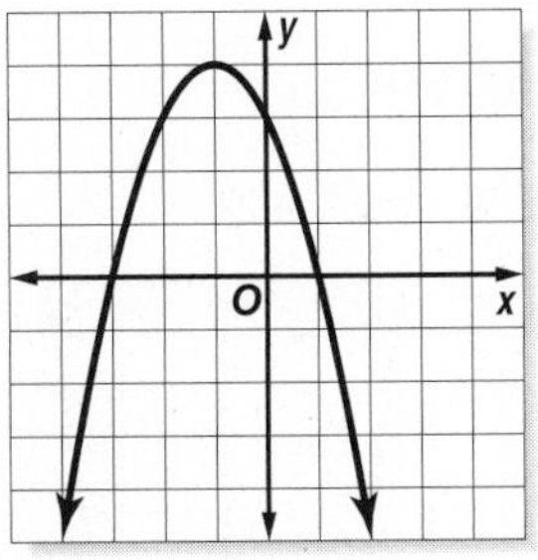

B.

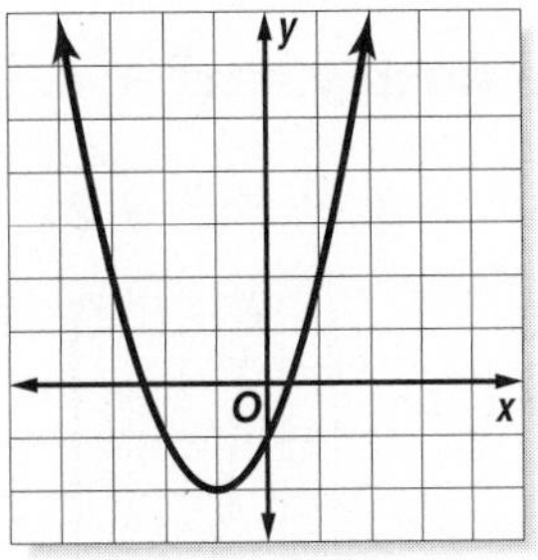

a. Each graph is a curve called a ______________.

b. The highest point of graph A is located at ______________. This point is the ______________ (maximum/minimum) point of the graph.

c. The lowest point of graph B is located at ______________. This point is the ______________ (maximum/minimum) point of the graph.

3. The maximum or minimum point of a parabola is called the ______________ of the parabola.

4. If you fold a parabola along a line to get two halves that match exactly, the line where you fold the parabola is the ____________________ of the parabola. This line goes through the ______________ of the parabola.

5. For a quadratic function $y = ax^2 + bx + c$, the parabola opens upward if a ________ 0. It opens downward if a ________ 0.

Helping You Remember

6. Look up the word *vertex* in a dictionary. You will find that it comes from the Latin word *vertere*, which means to turn. How can you use the idea of "to turn" to remember what the vertex of a parabola is?

Lesson 10-1

NAME ______________________________ DATE ____________ PERIOD _____

10-1 Enrichment

Translating Quadratic Graphs

When a figure is moved to a new position without undergoing any rotation, then the figure is said to have been **translated** to that position.

The graph of a quadratic equation in the form $y = (x - b)^2 + c$ is a translation of the graph of $y = x^2$.

Start with $y = x^2$.

Slide to the right 4 units.

$y = (x - 4)^2$

Then slide up 3 units.

$y = (x - 4)^2 + 3$

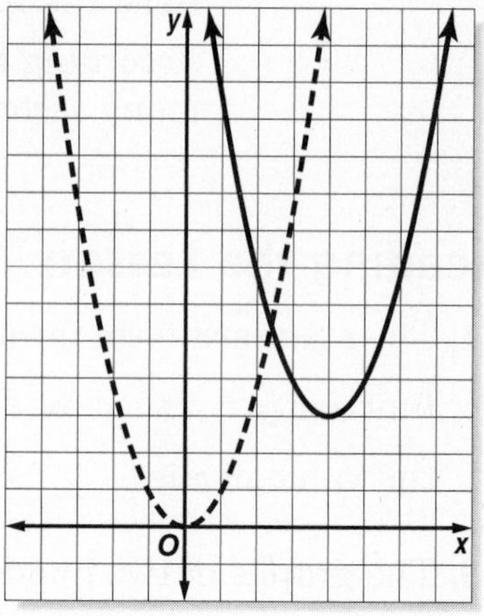

These equations have the form $y = x^2 + c$. Graph each equation.

1. $y = x^2 + 1$

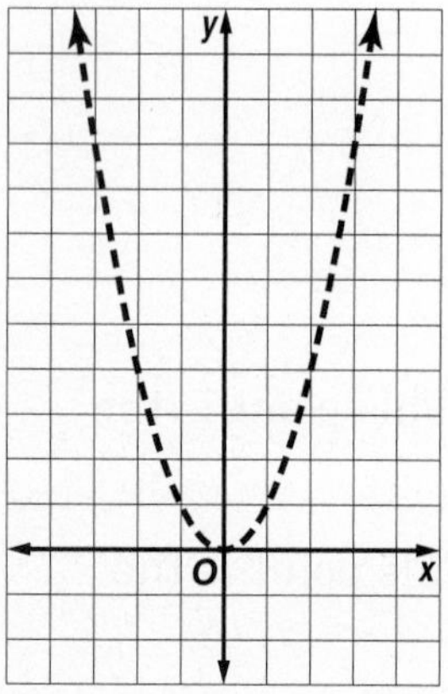

2. $y = x^2 + 2$

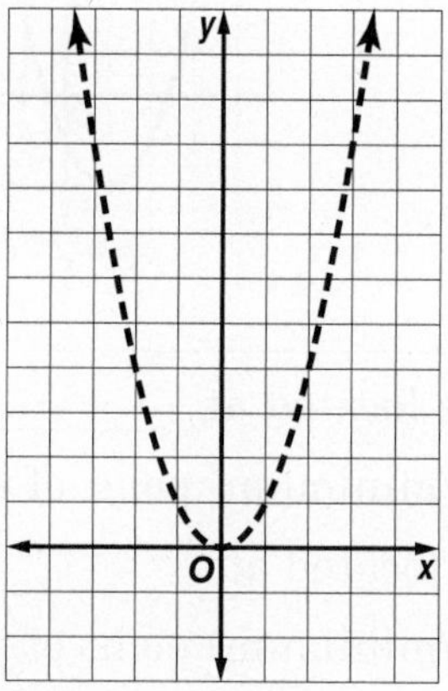

3. $y = x^2 - 2$

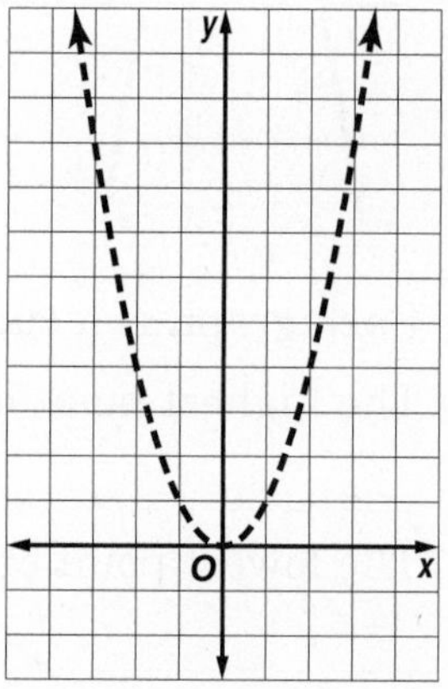

These equations have the form $y = (x - b)^2$. Graph each equation.

4. $y = (x - 1)^2$

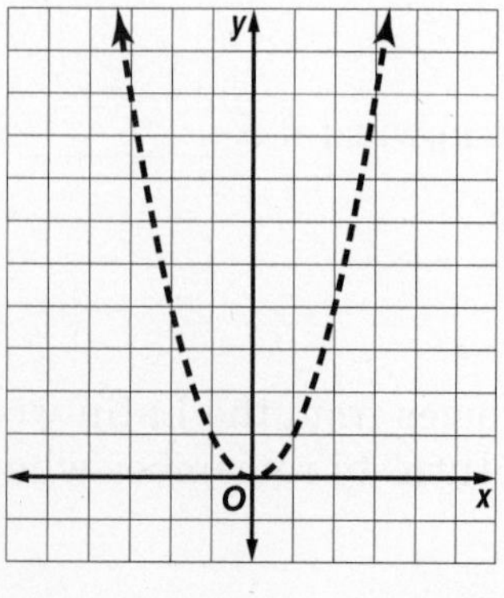

5. $y = (x - 3)^2$

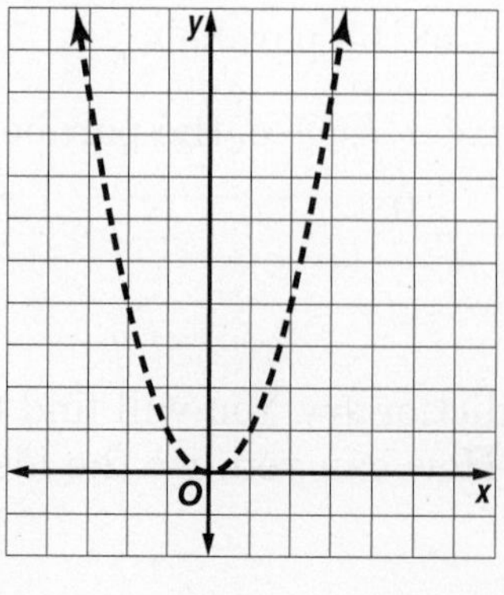

6. $y = (x + 2)^2$

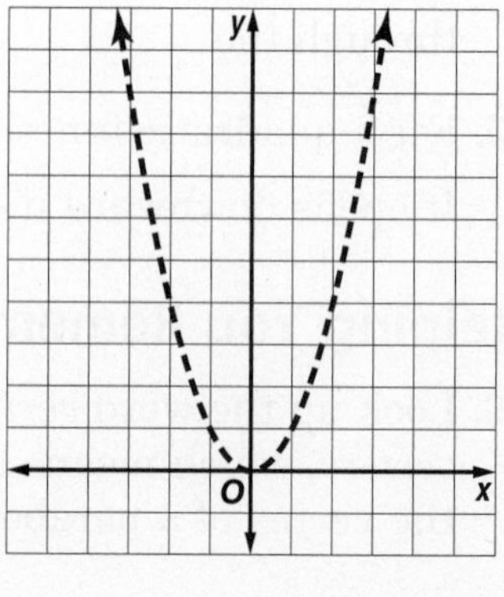

NAME ____________________ DATE ____________ PERIOD _____

10-2 Study Guide and Intervention

Solving Quadratic Equations by Graphing

Solve by Graphing

Quadratic Equation	an equation of the form $ax^2 + bx + c = 0$, where $a \neq 0$

The solutions of a quadratic equation are called the **roots** of the equation. The roots of a quadratic equation can be found by graphing the related quadratic function $f(x) = ax^2 + bx + c$ and finding the x-intercepts or **zeros** of the function.

Example 1 **Solve $x^2 + 4x + 3 = 0$ by graphing.**

Graph the related function $f(x) = x^2 + 4x + 3$. The equation of the axis of symmetry is $x = -\frac{4}{2(1)}$ or -2. The vertex is at $(-2, -1)$. Graph the vertex and several other points on either side of the axis of symmetry.

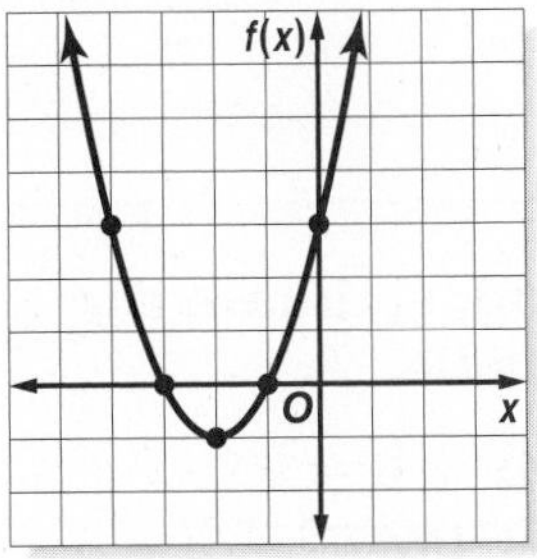

To solve $x^2 + 4x + 3 = 0$, you need to know where the value of $f(x) = 0$. This occurs at the x-intercepts, -3 and -1.

The solutions are -3 and -1.

Example 2 **Solve $x^2 - 6x + 9 = 0$ by graphing.**

Graph the related function $f(x) = x^2 - 6x + 9$. The equation of the axis of symmetry is $x = \frac{6}{2(1)}$ or 3. The vertex is at $(3, 0)$. Graph the vertex and several other points on either side of the axis of symmetry.

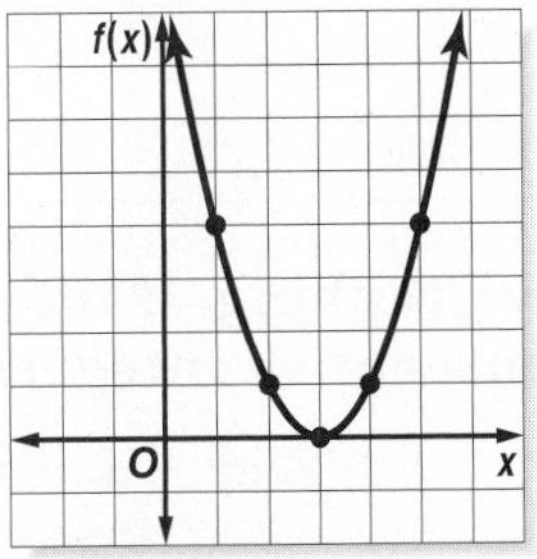

To solve $x^2 - 6x + 9 = 0$, you need to know where the value of $f(x) = 0$. The vertex of the parabola is the x-intercept. Thus, the only solution is 3.

Lesson 10-2

Exercises

Solve each equation by graphing.

1. $x^2 + 7x + 12 = 0$

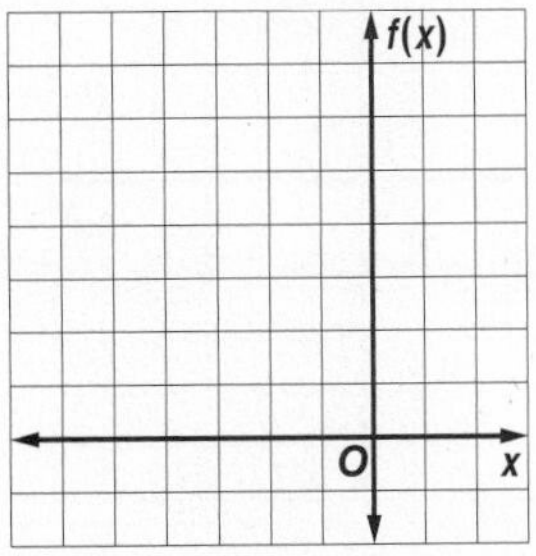

2. $x^2 - x - 12 = 0$

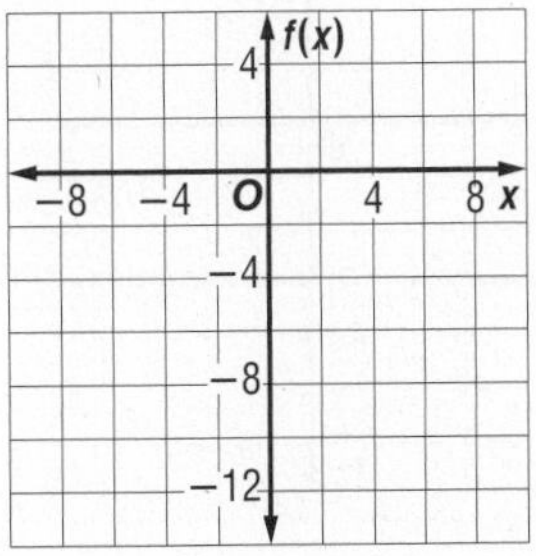

3. $x^2 - 4x + 5 = 0$

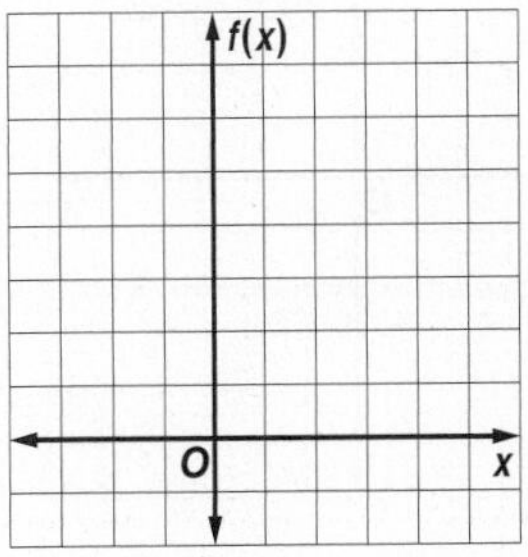

NAME ______________________________ DATE __________ PERIOD _____

10-2 Study Guide and Intervention *(continued)*

Solving Quadratic Equations by Graphing

Estimate Solutions The roots of a quadratic equation may not be integers. If exact roots cannot be found, they can be estimated by finding the consecutive integers between which the roots lie.

Example **Solve $x^2 + 6x + 6 = 0$ by graphing. If integral roots cannot be found, estimate the roots by stating the consecutive integers between which the roots lie.**

Graph the related function $f(x) = x^2 + 6x + 6$.

x	$f(x)$
−5	1
−4	−2
−3	−3
−2	−2
−1	1

Notice that the value of the function changes from negative to positive between the x-values of −5 and −4 and between −2 and −1.

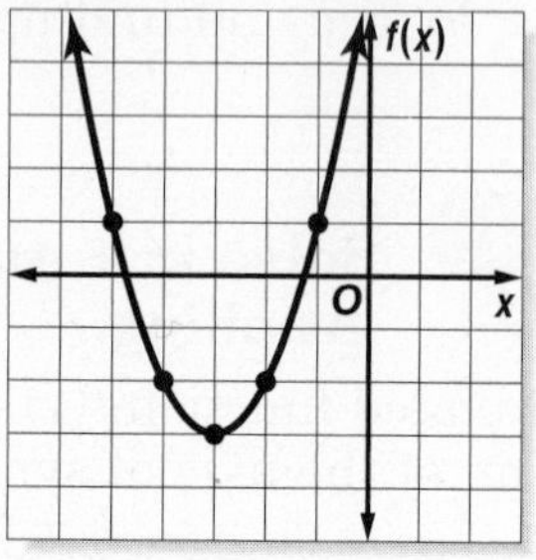

The x-intercepts of the graph are between −5 and −4 and between −2 and −1. So one root is between −5 and −4, and the other root is between −2 and −1.

Exercises

Solve each equation by graphing. If integral roots cannot be found, estimate the roots by stating the consecutive integers between which the roots lie.

1. $x^2 + 7x + 9 = 0$

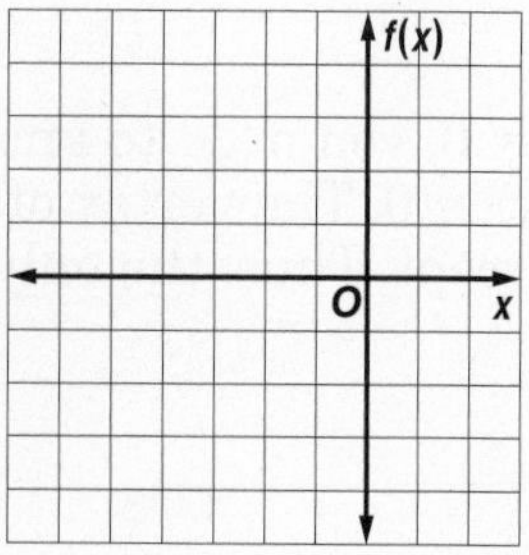

2. $x^2 - x - 4 = 0$

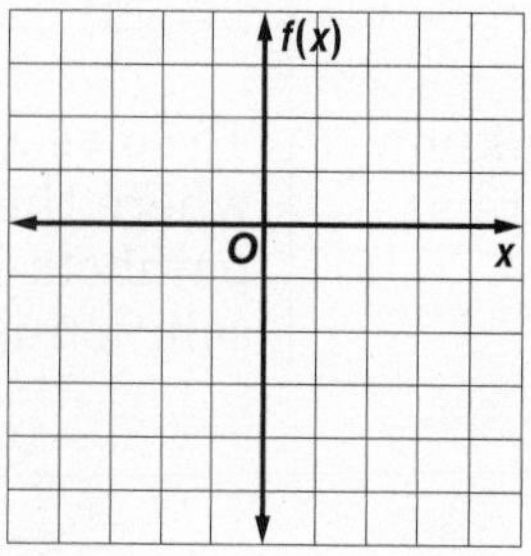

3. $x^2 - 4x + 6 = 0$

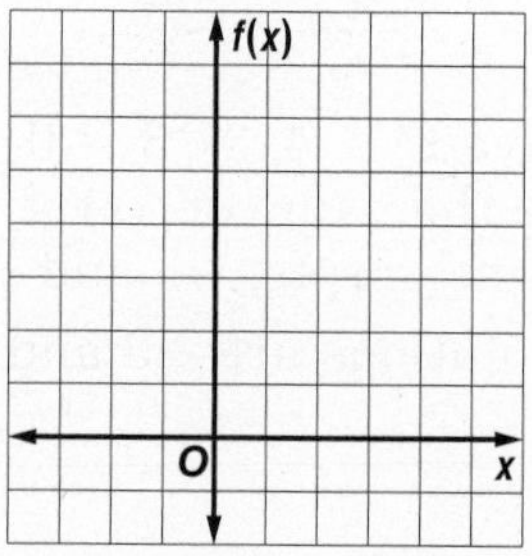

4. $x^2 - 4x - 1 = 0$

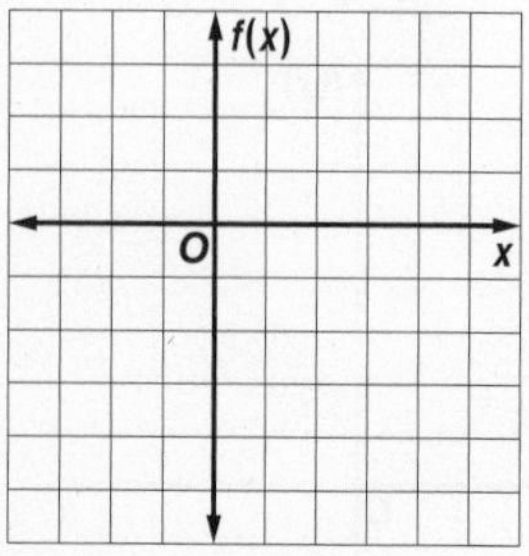

5. $4x^2 - 12x + 3 = 0$

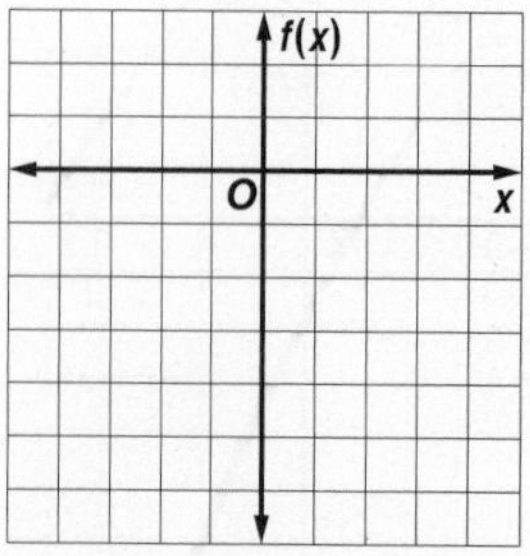

6. $x^2 - 2x - 4 = 0$

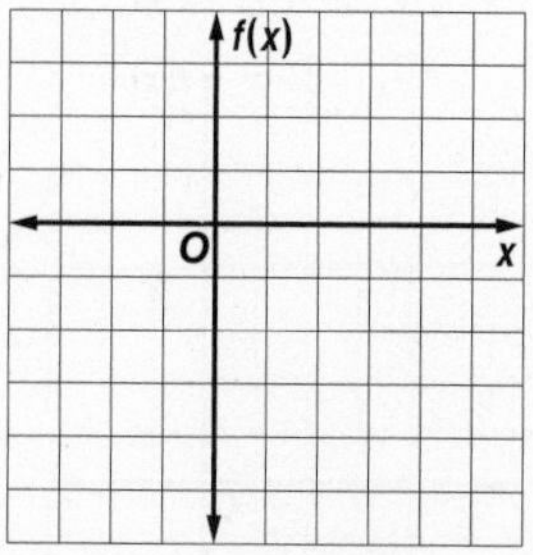

NAME ______________________________ DATE ____________ PERIOD _____

10-2 Skills Practice

Solving Quadratic Equations by Graphing

Solve each equation by graphing.

1. $x^2 - 4x + 5 = 0$

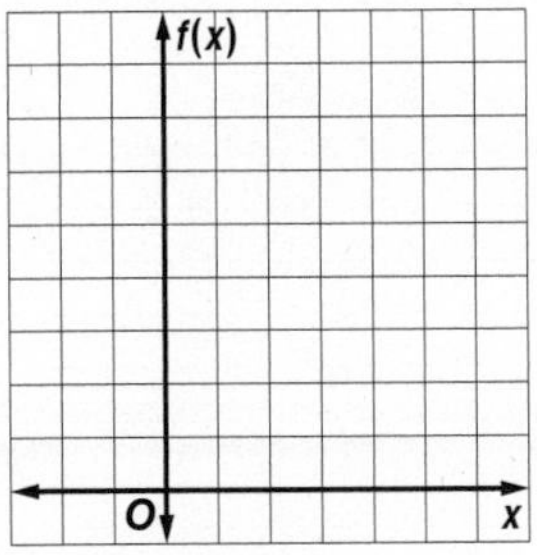

2. $c^2 + 6c + 8 = 0$

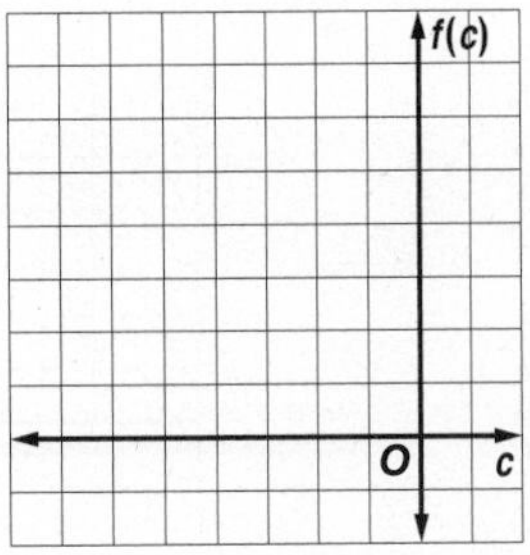

3. $a^2 - 2a = -1$

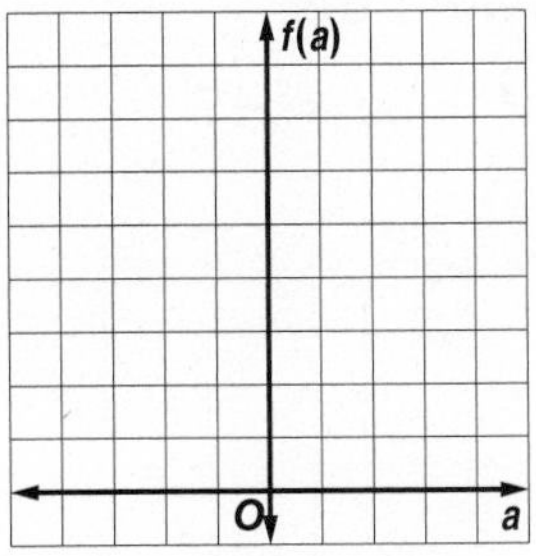

4. $n^2 - 7n = -10$

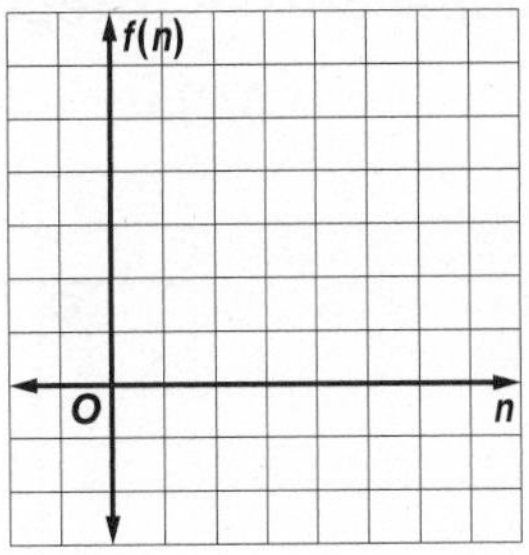

Solve each equation by graphing. If integral roots cannot be found, estimate the roots by stating the consecutive integers between which the roots lie.

5. $p^2 + 4p + 2 = 0$

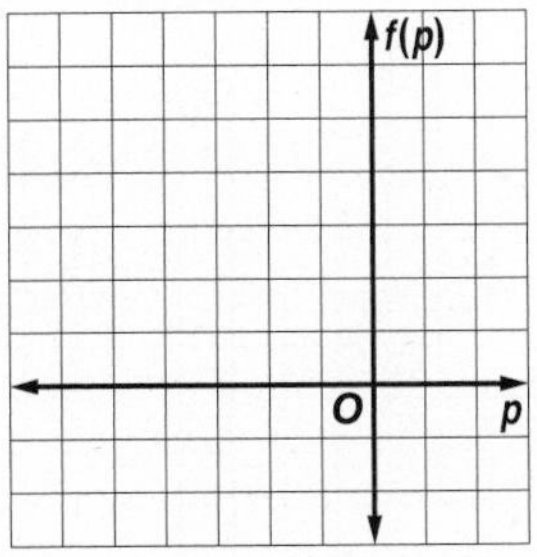

6. $x^2 + x - 3 = 0$

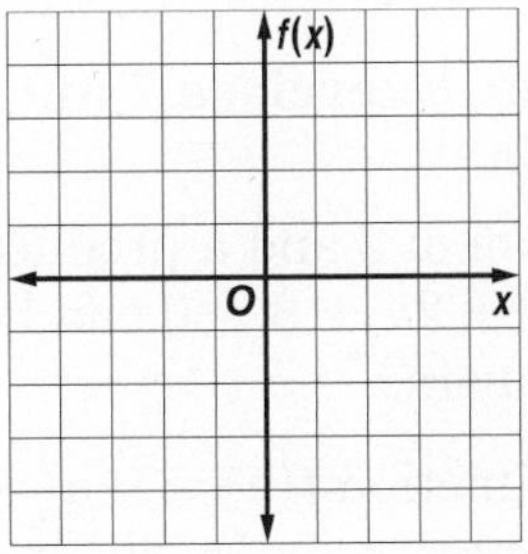

7. $d^2 + 6d = -3$

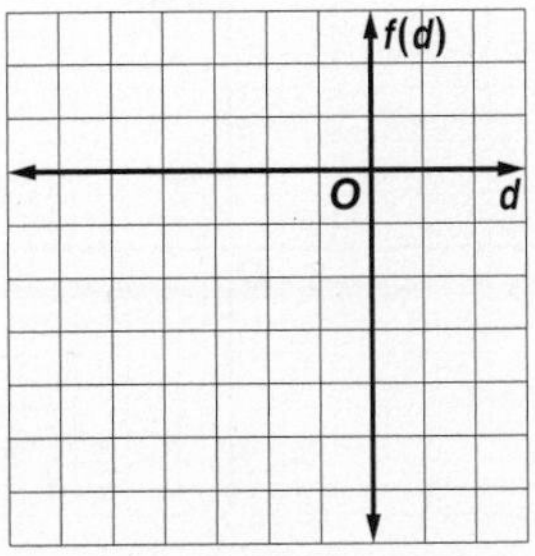

8. $h^2 + 1 = 4h$

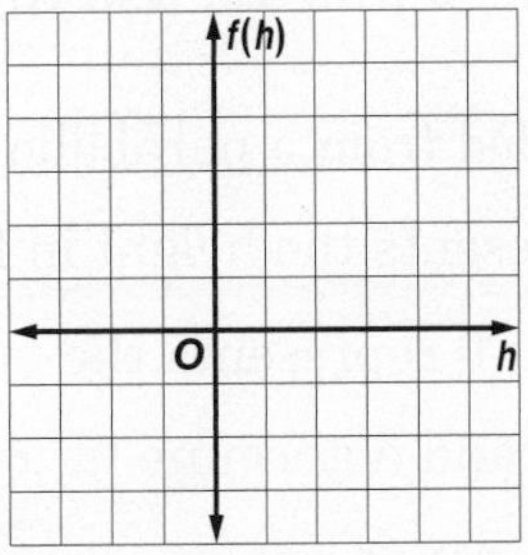

Lesson 10-2

NAME ______________________________ DATE ____________ PERIOD _____

10-2 Practice

Solving Quadratic Equations by Graphing

Solve each equation by graphing.

1. $x^2 - 5x + 6 = 0$

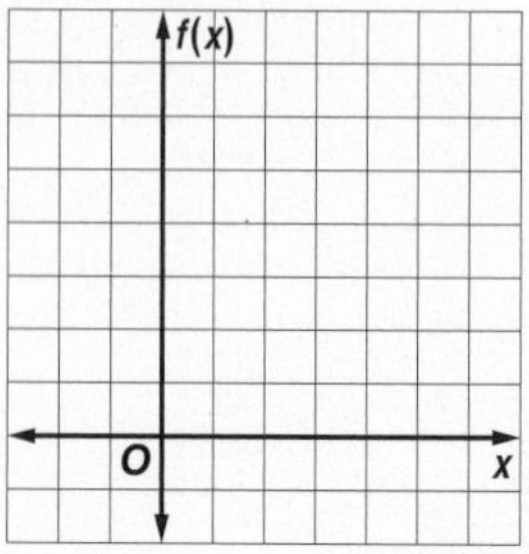

2. $w^2 + 6w + 9 = 0$

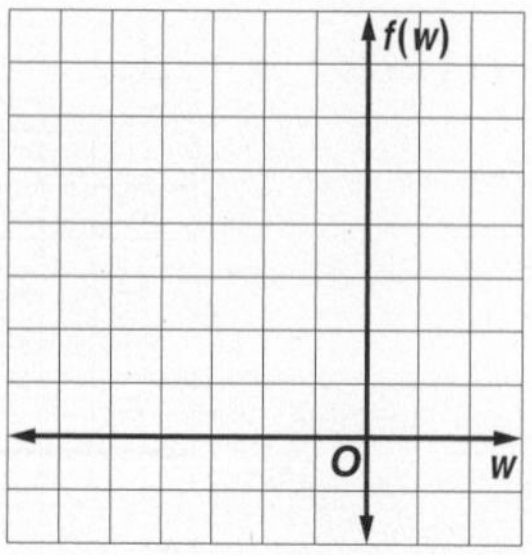

3. $b^2 - 4b + 5 = 0$

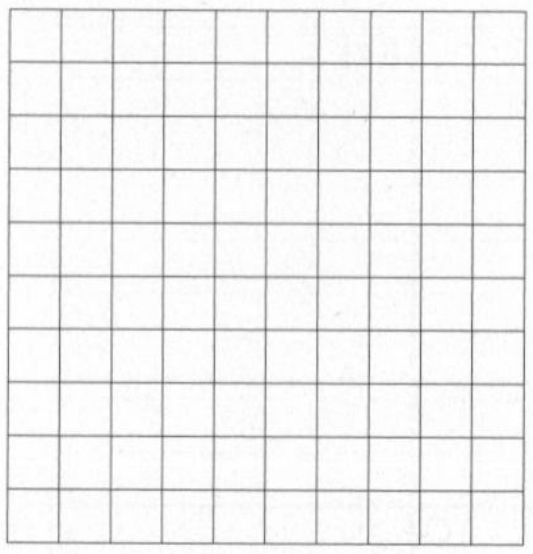

Solve each equation by graphing. If integral roots cannot be found, estimate the roots by stating the consecutive integers between which the roots lie.

4. $p^2 + 4p = 3$

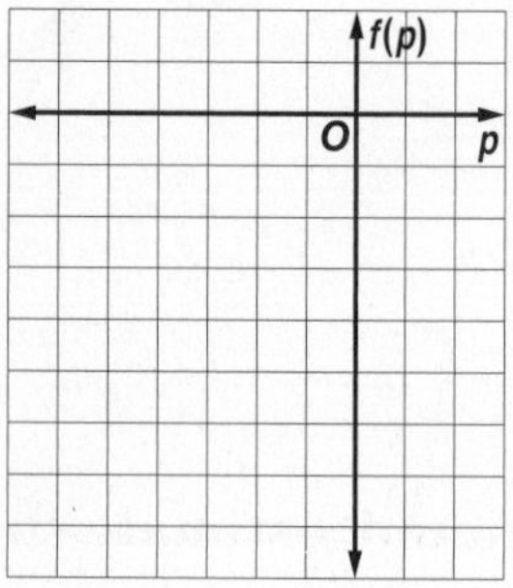

5. $2m^2 + 5 = 10m$

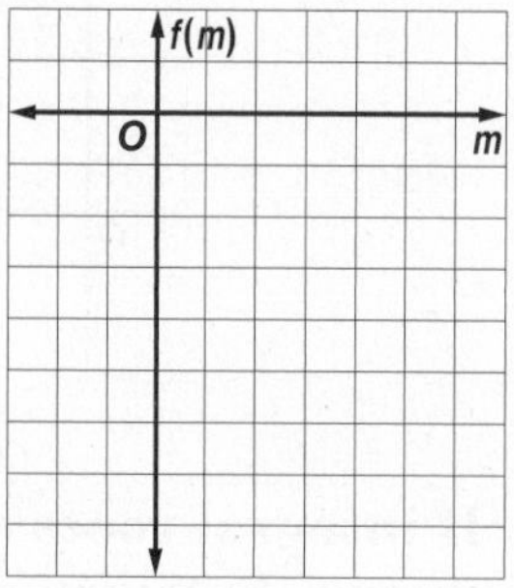

6. $2v^2 + 8v = -7$

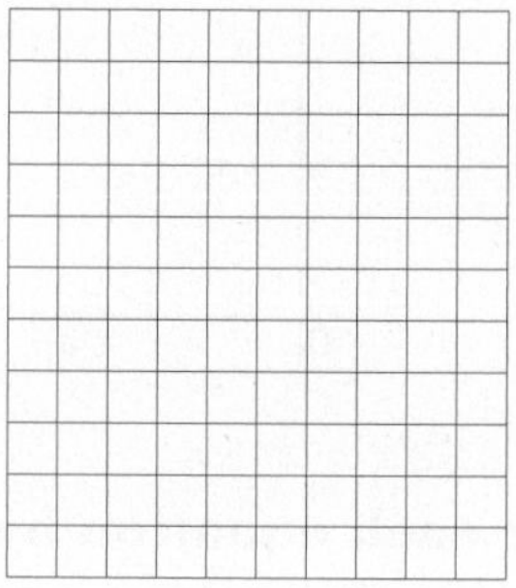

NUMBER THEORY For Exercises 7 and 8, use the following information.

Two numbers have a sum of 2 and a product of −8. The quadratic equation $-n^2 + 2n + 8 = 0$ can be used to determine the two numbers.

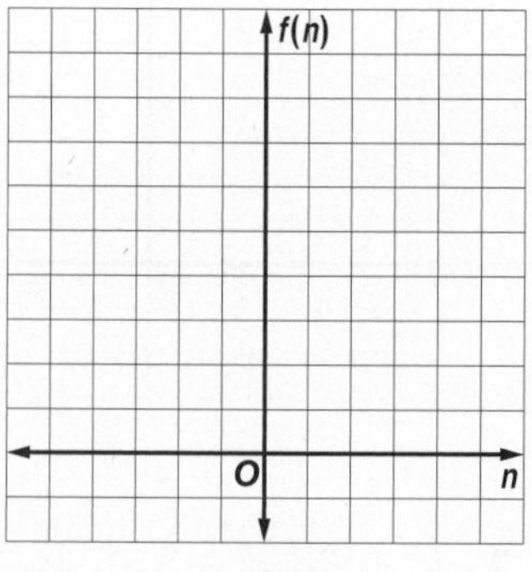

7. Graph the related function $f(n) = -n^2 + 2n + 8$ and determine its x-intercepts.

8. What are the two numbers?

DESIGN For Exercises 9 and 10, use the following information.

A footbridge is suspended from a parabolic support. The function $h(x) = -\frac{1}{25}x^2 + 9$ represents the height in feet of the support above the walkway, where $x = 0$ represents the midpoint of the bridge.

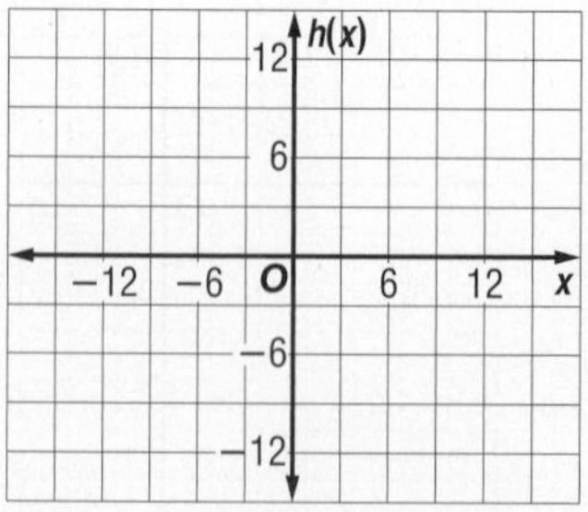

9. Graph the function and determine its x-intercepts.

10. What is the length of the walkway between the two supports?

NAME ______________________ DATE ____________ PERIOD _____

10-2 Reading to Learn Mathematics

Solving Quadratic Equations by Graphing

Pre-Activity **How can quadratic equations be used in computer simulations?**

Read the introduction to Lesson 10-2 at the top of page 533 in your textbook.

If one of the x-intercepts represents the location where the ball will hit the ground, what does the other x-intercept represent?

Reading the Lesson

1. The x-intercepts of the graph of a quadratic function are the x-coordinates of the points where the graph of the function intersects the x-axis. At those points, the y-coordinates are equal to ___________. This explains why the x-intercepts are called ___________ of the quadratic function.

2. The graphs of three functions are shown below. Use the graphs to provide the requested information about the related quadratic equations.

A. $f(x) = x^2 - 6x + 9$

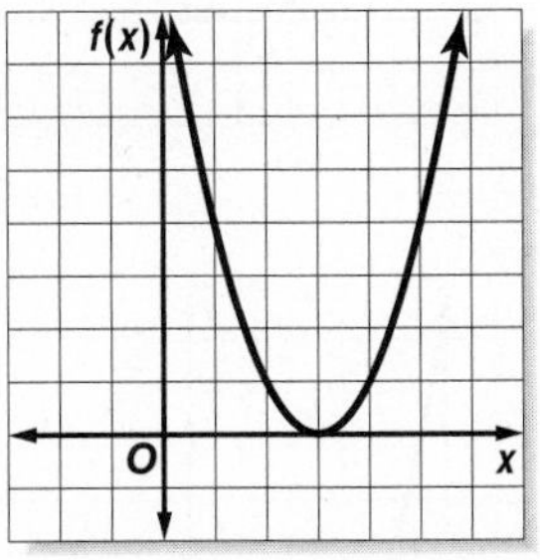

B. $f(x) = x^2 + 2x + 3$

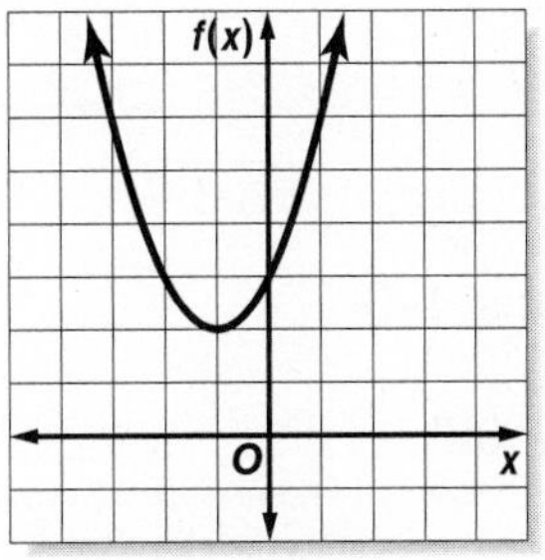

C. $f(x) = x^2 + x - 2$

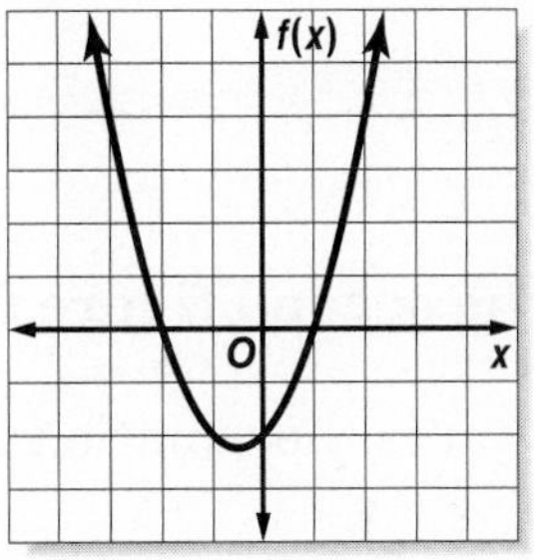

a. For Graph A, the related quadratic equation is ______________________.

How many solutions are there?

Name any solutions.

b. For Graph B, the related quadratic equation is ______________________.

How many solutions are there?

Name any solutions.

c. For Graph C, the related quadratic equation is ______________________.

How many solutions are there?

Name any solutions.

Helping You Remember

3. Describe how you can remember that the word *zero* is used when you are talking about functions, but the word *root* is used when you are talking about equations.

NAME ______________________ DATE __________ PERIOD _____

10-2 Enrichment

Odd Numbers and Parabolas

The solid parabola and the dashed stair-step graph are related. The parabola intersects the stair steps at their inside corners.

Use the figure for Exercises 1–3.

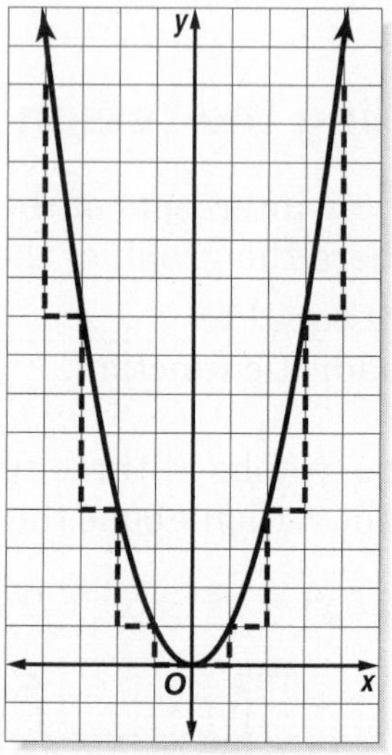

1. What is the equation of the parabola?

2. Describe the horizontal sections of the stair-step graph.

3. Describe the vertical sections of the stair-step graph.

Use the second figure for Exercises 4–6.

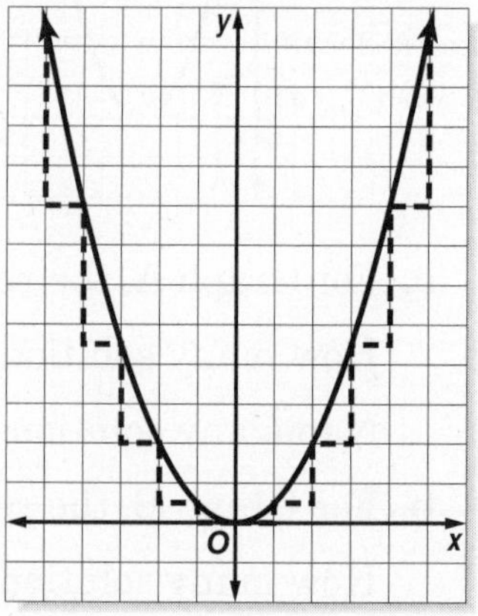

4. What is the equation of the parabola?

5. Describe the horizontal sections of the stair steps.

6. Describe the vertical sections.

7. How does the graph of $y = \frac{1}{2}x^2$ relate to the sequence of numbers $\frac{1}{2}, \frac{3}{2}, \frac{5}{2}, \frac{7}{2}, \ldots$?

8. Complete this conclusion. To graph a parabola with the equation $y = ax^2$, start at the vertex. Then go over 1 and up a; over 1 and up $3a$;

NAME ______________________ DATE ____________ PERIOD _____

10-3 Study Guide and Intervention

Solving Quadratic Equations by Completing the Square

Find the Square Root An equation such as $x^2 - 4x + 4 = 5$ can be solved by taking the square root of each side.

Example 1 **Solve $x^2 - 2x + 1 = 9$. Round to the nearest tenth if necessary.**

$$x^2 - 2x + 1 = 9$$
$$(x - 1)^2 = 9$$
$$\sqrt{(x - 1)^2} = \sqrt{9}$$
$$|x - 1| = \sqrt{9}$$
$$x - 1 = \pm 3$$
$$x - 1 + 1 = \pm 3 + 1$$
$$x = 1 \pm 3$$

$x = 1 + 3$ or $x = 1 - 3$
$= 4$ $= -2$

The solution set is $\{-2, 4\}$.

Example 2 **Solve $x^2 - 4x + 4 = 5$. Round to the nearest tenth if necessary.**

$$x^2 - 4x + 4 = 5$$
$$(x - 2)^2 = 5$$
$$\sqrt{(x - 2)^2} = \sqrt{5}$$
$$|x - 2| = \sqrt{5}$$
$$x - 2 = \pm\sqrt{5}$$
$$x - 2 + 2 = \pm\sqrt{5} + 2$$
$$x = 2 \pm \sqrt{5}$$

Use a calculator to evaluate each value of x.

$x = 2 + \sqrt{5}$ or $x = 2 - \sqrt{5}$
≈ 4.2 ≈ -0.2

The solution set is $\{-0.2, 4.2\}$.

Exercises

Solve each equation by taking the square root of each side. Round to the nearest tenth if necessary.

1. $x^2 + 4x + 4 = 9$

2. $m^2 + 12m + 36 = 1$

3. $r^2 - 6r + 9 = 16$

4. $x^2 - 2x + 1 = 25$

5. $x^2 - 8x + 16 = 5$

6. $x^2 - 10x + 25 = 8$

7. $c^2 - 4c + 4 = 7$

8. $p^2 + 16p + 64 = 3$

9. $x^2 + 8x + 16 = 9$

10. $x^2 + 6x + 9 = 4$

11. $a^2 + 8a + 16 = 10$

12. $y^2 - 12y + 36 = 5$

13. $x^2 + 10x + 25 = 1$

14. $y^2 + 14y + 49 = 6$

15. $m^2 - 8m + 16 = 2$

16. $x^2 + 12x + 36 = 10$

17. $a^2 - 14a + 49 = 3$

18. $y^2 + 8y + 16 = 7$

NAME ______________________ DATE ____________ PERIOD _____

10-3 Study Guide and Intervention *(continued)*

Solving Quadratic Equations by Completing the Square

Complete the Square Since few quadratic expressions are perfect square trinomials, the method of **completing the square** can be used to solve some quadratic equations. Use the following steps to complete the square for a quadratic expression of the form $ax^2 + bx$.

Step 1	Find $\frac{b}{2}$.
Step 2	Find $\left(\frac{b}{2}\right)^2$.
Step 3	Add $\left(\frac{b}{2}\right)^2$ to $ax^2 + bx$.

Example **Solve $x^2 + 6x + 3 = 10$ by completing the square.**

$x^2 + 6x + 3 = 10$	Original equation
$x^2 + 6x + 3 - 3 = 10 - 3$	Subtract 3 from each side.
$x^2 + 6x = 7$	Simplify.
$x^2 + 6x + 9 = 7 + 9$	Since $\left(\frac{6}{2}\right)^2 = 9$, add 9 to each side.
$(x + 3)^2 = 16$	Factor $x^2 + 6x + 9$.
$x + 3 = \pm 4$	Take the square root of each side.
$x = -3 \pm 4$	Simplify.

$x = -3 + 4$ or $x = -3 - 4$
$= 1$ $\qquad\qquad = -7$

The solution set is $\{-7, 1\}$.

Exercises

Solve each equation by completing the square. Round to the nearest tenth if necessary.

1. $t^2 - 4t + 3 = 0$

2. $y^2 + 10y = -9$

3. $y^2 - 8y - 9 = 0$

4. $x^2 - 6x = 16$

5. $p^2 - 4p - 5 = 0$

6. $x^2 - 12x = 9$

7. $c^2 + 8c = 20$

8. $p^2 = 2p + 1$

9. $x^2 + 20x + 11 = -8$

10. $x^2 - 1 = 5x$

11. $a^2 = 22a + 23$

12. $m^2 - 8m = -7$

13. $x^2 + 10x = 24$

14. $a^2 - 18a = 19$

15. $b^2 + 16b = -16$

16. $4x^2 = 24 + 4x$

17. $2m^2 + 4m + 2 = 8$

18. $4k^2 = 40k + 44$

NAME ______________________________ DATE ____________ PERIOD _____

10-3 Skills Practice

Solving Quadratic Equations by Completing the Square

Solve each equation by taking the square root of each side. Round to the nearest tenth if necessary.

1. $c^2 - 12c + 36 = 4$

2. $w^2 - 10w + 25 = 16$

3. $b^2 + 16b + 64 = 9$

4. $y^2 + 2y + 1 = 3$

5. $r^2 + 4r + 4 = 7$

6. $a^2 - 8a + 16 = 12$

Find the value of *c* that makes each trinomial a perfect square.

7. $g^2 + 6g + c$

8. $y^2 + 4y + c$

9. $a^2 - 14a + c$

10. $n^2 - 2n + c$

11. $s^2 - 18s + c$

12. $p^2 + 20p + c$

Solve each equation by completing the square. Round to the nearest tenth if necessary.

13. $x^2 + 4x - 12 = 0$

14. $v^2 - 8v + 15 = 0$

15. $q^2 + 6q = 7$

16. $r^2 - 2r = 15$

17. $m^2 - 14m + 30 = 6$

18. $b^2 + 12b + 21 = 10$

19. $z^2 - 4z + 1 = 0$

20. $y^2 - 6y + 4 = 0$

21. $r^2 - 8r + 10 = 0$

22. $p^2 - 2p = 5$

23. $2a^2 + 20a = -2$

24. $0.5g^2 + 8g = -7$

Lesson 10-3

NAME ______________________ DATE ____________ PERIOD _____

10-3 Practice

Solving Quadratic Equations by Completing the Square

Solve each equation by taking the square root of each side. Round to the nearest tenth if necessary.

1. $b^2 - 14b + 49 = 64$

2. $s^2 + 16s + 64 = 100$

3. $h^2 - 8h + 16 = 15$

4. $a^2 + 6a + 9 = 27$

5. $p^2 - 20p + 100 = 28$

6. $u^2 + 10u + 25 = 90$

Find the value of *c* that makes each trinomial a perfect square.

7. $t^2 - 24t + c$

8. $b^2 + 28b + c$

9. $y^2 + 40y + c$

10. $m^2 + 3m + c$

11. $g^2 - 9g + c$

12. $v^2 - v + c$

Solve each equation by completing the square. Round to the nearest tenth if necessary.

13. $w^2 - 14w + 24 = 0$

14. $p^2 + 12p = 13$

15. $s^2 - 30s + 56 = -25$

16. $v^2 + 8v + 9 = 0$

17. $t^2 - 10t + 6 = -7$

18. $n^2 + 18n + 50 = 9$

19. $3u^2 + 15u - 3 = 0$

20. $4c^2 - 72 = 24c$

21. $0.9a^2 + 5.4a - 4 = 0$

22. $0.4h^2 + 0.8h = 0.2$

23. $\frac{1}{2}x^2 - \frac{1}{2}x - 10 = 0$

24. $\frac{1}{4}x^2 + \frac{3}{2}x - 2 = 0$

BUSINESS For Exercises 25 and 26, use the following information.

Jaime owns a business making decorative boxes to store jewelry, mementos, and other valuables. The function $y = x^2 + 50x + 1800$ models the profit y that Jaime has made in month x for the first two years of his business.

25. Write an equation representing the month in which Jaime's profit is $2400.

26. Use completing the square to find out in which month Jaime's profit is $2400.

27. PHYSICS From a height of 256 feet above a lake on a cliff, Mikaela throws a rock out over the lake. The height H of the rock t seconds after Mikaela throws it is represented by the equation $H = -16t^2 + 32t + 256$. To the nearest tenth of a second, how long does it take the rock to reach the lake below? (*Hint:* Replace H with 0.)

10-3 Reading to Learn Mathematics

Solving Quadratic Equations by Completing the Square

Pre-Activity **How did ancient mathematicians use squares to solve algebraic equations?**

Read the introduction to Lesson 10-3 at the top of page 539 in your textbook.

To solve the problem, how many "units" would Al-Khwarizmi have added to each side of the equation?

Reading the Lesson

1. Draw a line under each quadratic equation that you could solve by taking the square root of each side.

$x^2 + 6x + 9 = 100$	$x^2 - 14x + 40 = 25$	$x^2 - 16x + 64 = 26$
$x^2 - 20x + 80 = 16$	$x^2 + 10x + 36 = 49$	$x^2 - 12x + 36 = 6$

2. How can you tell whether it is possible to solve a quadratic equation by taking the square root of each side?

3. Explain how to find what number is needed for the ■ in order to make $x^2 - 20x +$ ■ a perfect square.

4. To solve $3x^2 - 6x = 54$ by completing the square, why does it help first to divide both sides by 3?

Helping You Remember

5. The method of completing the square might be easier to remember if you can connect it to what you know about perfect square trinomials. How is completing the square related to the method you use to determine whether a trinomial is a perfect square trinomial?

Lesson 10-3

NAME ______________________________ DATE ____________ PERIOD _____

10-3 Enrichment

Parabolas Through Three Given Points

If you know two points on a straight line, you can find the equation of the line. To find the equation of a parabola, you need three points on the curve.

Here is how to approximate an equation of the parabola through the points (0, −2), (3, 0), and (5, 2).

Use the general equation $y = ax^2 + bx + c$. By substituting the given values for x and y, you get three equations.

(0, −2): $-2 = c$

(3, 0): $0 = 9a + 3b + c$

(5, 2): $2 = 25a + 5b + c$

First, substitute −2 for c in the second and third equations. Then solve those two equations as you would any system of two equations. Multiply the second equation by 5 and the third equation by −3.

$0 = 9a + 3b - 2$ Multiply by 5. $0 = 45a + 15b - 10$

$0 = 25a + 5b - 2$ Multiply by −3. $-6 = -75a - 15b + 6$

$-6 = -30a - 4$

$a = \frac{1}{15}$

To find b, substitute $\frac{1}{15}$ for a in either the second or third equation.

$0 = 9\left(\frac{1}{15}\right) + 3b - 2$

$b = \frac{7}{15}$

The equation of a parabola through the three points is

$y = \frac{1}{15}x^2 + \frac{7}{15}x - 2.$

Find the equation of a parabola through each set of three points.

1. (1, 5), (0, 6), (2, 3)

2. (−5, 0), (0, 0), (8, 100)

3. (4, −4), (0, 1), (3, −2)

4. (1, 3), (6, 0), (0, 0)

5. (2, 2), (5, −3), (0, −1)

6. (0, 4), (4, 0), (−4, 4)

NAME ______________________________ DATE ____________ PERIOD _____

10-4 Study Guide and Intervention

Solving Quadratic Equations by Using the Quadratic Formula

Quadratic Formula To solve the standard form of the quadratic equation, $ax^2 + bx + c = 0$, use the **Quadratic Formula.**

Quadratic Formula	the formula $x = \frac{-b \pm \sqrt{b^2 - 4ac}}{2a}$ that gives the solutions of $ax^2 + bx + c = 0$, where $a \neq 0$

Example 1 **Solve $x^2 + 2x = 3$ by using the Quadratic Formula.**

Rewrite the equation in standard form.

$x^2 + 2x = 3$ Original equation

$x^2 + 2x - 3 = 3 - 3$ Subtract 3 from each side.

$x^2 + 2x - 3 = 0$ Simplify.

Now let $a = 1$, $b = 2$, and $c = -3$ in the Quadratic Formula.

$$x = \frac{-b \pm \sqrt{b^2 - 4ac}}{2a}$$

$$= \frac{-2 \pm \sqrt{(2)^2 - 4(1)(-3)}}{2(1)}$$

$$= \frac{-2 \pm \sqrt{16}}{2}$$

$$x = \frac{-2 + 4}{2} \quad \text{or} \quad x = \frac{-2 - 4}{2}$$

$$= 1 \qquad\qquad = -3$$

The solution set is $\{-3, 1\}$.

Example 2 **Solve $x^2 - 6x - 2 = 0$ by using the Quadratic Formula. Round to the nearest tenth if necessary.**

For this equation $a = 1$, $b = -6$, and $c = -2$.

$$x = \frac{-b \pm \sqrt{b^2 - 4ac}}{2a}$$

$$= \frac{6 \pm \sqrt{(-6)^2 - 4(1)(-2)}}{2(1)}$$

$$= \frac{6 \pm \sqrt{44}}{2}$$

$$x = \frac{6 + \sqrt{44}}{2} \quad \text{or} \quad x = \frac{6 - \sqrt{44}}{2}$$

$$\approx 6.3 \qquad\qquad \approx -0.3$$

The solution set is $\{-0.3, 6.3\}$.

Exercises

Solve each equation by using the Quadratic Formula. Round to the nearest tenth if necessary.

1. $x^2 - 3x + 2 = 0$

2. $m^2 - 8m = -16$

3. $16r^2 - 8r = -1$

4. $x^2 + 5x = 6$

5. $3x^2 + 2x = 8$

6. $8x^2 - 8x - 5 = 0$

7. $-4c^2 + 19c = 21$

8. $2p^2 + 6p = 5$

9. $48x^2 + 22x - 15 = 0$

10. $8x^2 - 4x = 24$

11. $2p^2 + 5p = 8$

12. $8y^2 + 9y - 4 = 0$

13. $2x^2 + 9x + 4 = 0$

14. $8y^2 + 17y + 2 = 0$

15. $3z^2 + 5z - 2 = 0$

16. $-2x^2 + 8x + 4 = 0$

17. $a^2 + 3a = 2$

18. $2y^2 - 6y + 4 = 0$

10-4 Study Guide and Intervention (continued)

Solving Quadratic Equations by Using the Quadratic Formula

The Discriminant In the Quadratic Formula, $x = \frac{-b \pm \sqrt{b^2 - 4ac}}{2a}$, the expression under the radical sign, $b^2 - 4ac$, is called the **discriminant**. The discriminant can be used to determine the number of real roots for a quadratic equation.

Case 1: $b^2 - 4ac < 0$	Case 2: $b^2 - 4ac = 0$	Case 3: $b^2 - 4ac > 0$
no real roots	one real root	two real roots

Example **State the value of the discriminant for each equation. Then determine the number of real roots.**

a. $12x^2 + 5x = 4$

Write the equation in standard form.

$12x^2 + 5x = 4$ Original equation

$12x^2 + 5x - 4 = 4 - 4$ Subtract 4 from each side.

$12x^2 + 5x - 4 = 0$ Simplify.

Now find the discriminant.

$b^2 - 4ac = (5)^2 - 4(12)(-4)$

$= 217$

Since the discriminant is positive, the equation has two real roots.

b. $2x^2 + 3x = -4$

$2x^2 + 3x = -4$ Original equation

$2x^2 + 3x + 4 = -4 + 4$ Add 4 to each side.

$2x^2 + 3x + 4 = 0$ Simplify.

$b^2 - 4ac = (3)^2 - 4(2)(4)$

$= -23$

Since the discriminant is negative, the equation has no real roots.

Exercises

State the value of the discriminant for each equation. Then determine the number of real roots of the equation.

1. $3x^2 + 2x - 3 = 0$

2. $3n^2 - 7n - 8 = 0$

3. $2d^2 - 10d - 9 = 0$

4. $4x^2 = x + 4$

5. $3x^2 - 13x = 10$

6. $6x^2 - 10x + 10 = 0$

7. $2k^2 - 20 = -k$

8. $6p^2 = -11p - 40$

9. $9 - 18x + 9x^2 = 0$

10. $12x^2 + 9 = -6x$

11. $9a^2 = 81$

12. $16y^2 + 16y + 4 = 0$

13. $8x^2 + 9x = 2$

14. $4a^2 - 4a + 4 = 3$

15. $3b^2 - 18b = -14$

NAME ______________________________ DATE ____________ PERIOD _____

10-4 Skills Practice

Solving Quadratic Equations by Using the Quadratic Formula

Solve each equation by using the Quadratic Formula. Round to the nearest tenth if necessary.

1. $u^2 - 49 = 0$

2. $n^2 - n - 20 = 0$

3. $s^2 - 5s - 36 = 0$

4. $b^2 + 11b + 30 = 0$

5. $c^2 - 7c = -3$

6. $p^2 + 4p = -1$

7. $a^2 - 9a + 22 = 0$

8. $x^2 + 6x + 3 = 0$

9. $2x^2 + 5x - 7 = 0$

10. $2h^2 - 3h = -1$

11. $2p^2 + 5p + 4 = 0$

12. $2g^2 + 7g = 9$

13. $3t^2 + 2t - 3 = 0$

14. $3x^2 - 7x - 6 = 0$

State the value of the discriminant for each equation. Then determine the number of real roots of the equation.

15. $q^2 + 4q + 3 = 0$

16. $m^2 + 2m + 1 = 0$

17. $a^2 - 4a + 10 = 0$

18. $w^2 - 6w + 7 = 0$

19. $z^2 - 2z - 7 = 0$

20. $y^2 - 10y + 25 = 0$

21. $2d^2 + 5d - 8 = 0$

22. $2s^2 + 6s + 12 = 0$

23. $2u^2 - 4u + 10 = 0$

24. $3h^2 + 7h + 3 = 0$

Lesson 10-4

NAME ______________________ DATE __________ PERIOD _____

10-4 Practice

Solving Quadratic Equations by Using the Quadratic Formula

Solve each equation by using the Quadratic Formula. Round to the nearest tenth if necessary.

1. $g^2 + 2g - 3 = 0$

2. $a^2 + 8a + 7 = 0$

3. $v^2 - 4v + 6 = 0$

4. $d^2 - 6d + 7 = 0$

5. $2z^2 + 9z - 5 = 0$

6. $2r^2 + 12r + 10 = 0$

7. $2b^2 - 9b = -12$

8. $2h^2 - 5h = 12$

9. $3p^2 + p = 4$

10. $3m^2 - 1 = -8m$

11. $4y^2 + 7y = 15$

12. $1.6n^2 + 2n + 2.5 = 0$

13. $4.5k^2 + 4k - 1.5 = 0$

14. $\frac{1}{2}c^2 + 2c + \frac{3}{2} = 0$

15. $3w^2 - \frac{3}{4}w = \frac{1}{2}$

State the value of the discriminant for each equation. Then determine the number of real roots of the equation.

16. $a^2 + 8a + 16 = 0$

17. $c^2 + 3c + 12 = 0$

18. $2w^2 + 12w = -7$

19. $2u^2 + 15u = -30$

20. $4n^2 + 9 = 12n$

21. $3g^2 - 2g = 3.5$

22. $2.5k^2 + 3k - 0.5 = 0$

23. $\frac{3}{4}d^2 - 3d = -4$

24. $\frac{1}{4}s^2 = -s - 1$

CONSTRUCTION For Exercises 25 and 26, use the following information.

A roofer tosses a piece of roofing tile from a roof onto the ground 30 feet below. He tosses the tile with an initial downward velocity of 10 feet per second.

25. Write an equation to find how long it takes the tile to hit the ground. Use the model for vertical motion, $H = -16t^2 + vt + h$, where H is the height of an object after t seconds, v is the initial velocity, and h is the initial height. (*Hint:* Since the object is thrown down, the initial velocity is negative.)

26. How long does it take the tile to hit the ground?

27. PHYSICS Lupe tosses a ball up to Quyen, waiting at a third-story window, with an initial velocity of 30 feet per second. She releases the ball from a height of 6 feet. The equation $h = -16t^2 + 30t + 6$ represents the height h of the ball after t seconds. If the ball must reach a height of 25 feet for Quyen to catch it, does the ball reach Quyen? Explain. (*Hint:* Substitute 25 for h and use the discriminant.)

NAME ______________________________ DATE ____________ PERIOD _____

10-4 Reading to Learn Mathematics

Solving Quadratic Equations by Using the Quadratic Formula

Pre-Activity **How can the Quadratic Formula be used to solve problems involving population trends?**

Read the introduction to Lesson 10-4 at the top of page 546 in your textbook.

Your teacher asks you to predict when 17% of the population will consist of people born outside the United States. What equation should you use to make the prediction?

Reading the Lesson

1. Suppose you want to solve $12x^2 + 7x = 15$ using the Quadratic Formula.

a. What should you do first?

b. What are the values you need to substitute for a, b, and c in the Quadratic Formula?

c. Apply the Quadratic Formula using the above values, but do not solve the equation.

2. a. You can use the discriminant to determine the number of real roots for a quadratic equation. What is the discriminant?

b. Complete the statements below so that each statement is true.

When the value of the discriminant is ______________, there is one real root.

When the value of the discriminant is ______________, there are two real roots.

When the value of the discriminant is ______________, there are no real roots.

Helping You Remember

3. To help remember the methods for solving a quadratic equation, explain how you would choose the best method for solving a quadratic equation $ax^2 + bx + c = 0$.

Lesson 10-4

NAME ______________________ DATE ____________ PERIOD _____

10-4 Enrichment

Mechanical Constructions of Parabolas

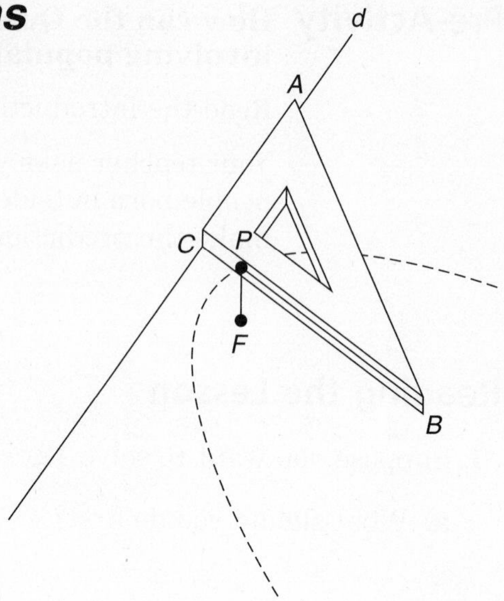

A given line and a point determine a parabola. Here is one way to construct the curve.

Use a right triangle ABC (or a stiff piece of rectangular cardboard).

Place one leg of the triangle on the given line d. Fasten one end of a string with length BC at the given point F and the other end to the triangle at point B.

Put the tip of a pencil at point P and keep the string tight.

As you move the triangle along the line d, the point of your pencil will trace a parabola.

Draw the parabola determined by line *d* and point *F*.

1.

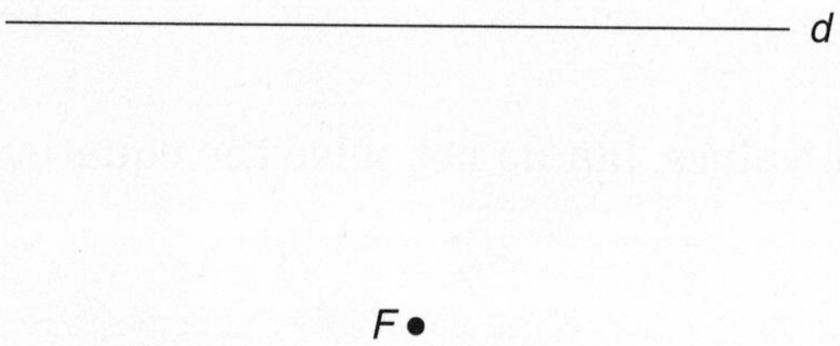

2.

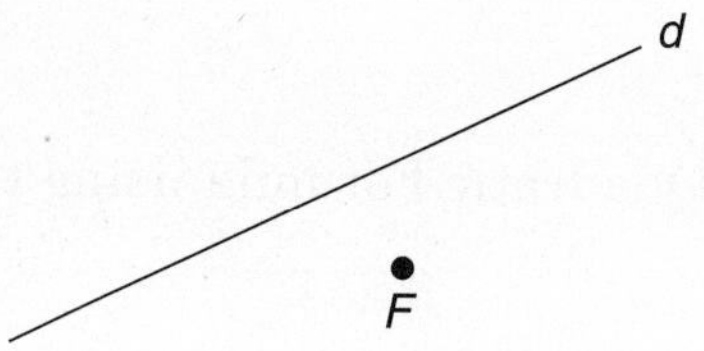

3.

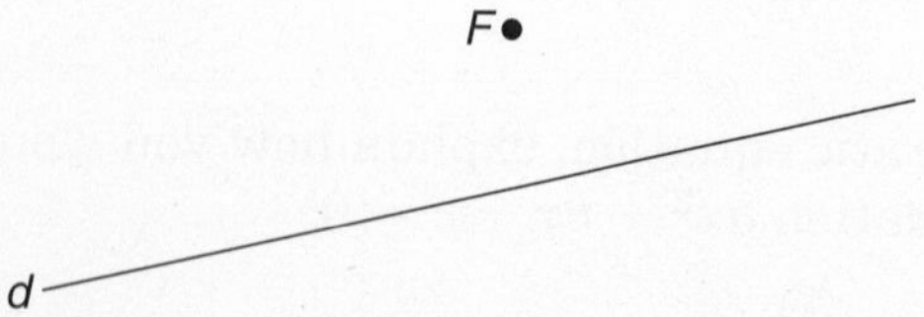

4.

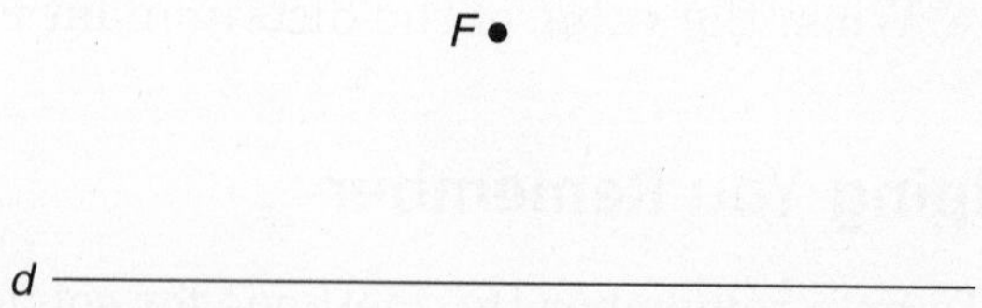

5. Use your drawings to complete this conclusion. The greater the distance of point F from line d, ______________________________

NAME ______________________ DATE ____________ PERIOD _____

10-5 Study Guide and Intervention

Exponential Functions

Graph Exponential Functions

Exponential Function	a function defined by an equation of the form $y = ax$, where $a > 0$ and $a \neq 1$

You can use values of x to find ordered pairs that satisfy an exponential function. Then you can use the ordered pairs to graph the function.

Example 1 **Graph $y = 3^x$. State the y-intercept.**

x	y
−2	$\frac{1}{9}$
−1	$\frac{1}{3}$
0	1
1	3
2	9

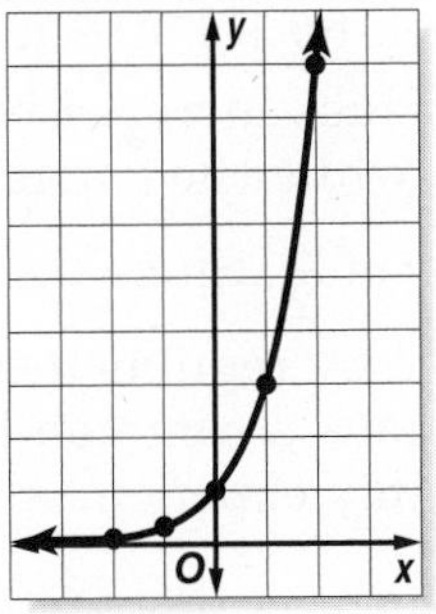

The y-intercept is 1.

Example 2 **Graph $y = \left(\frac{1}{4}\right)^x$. Use the graph to determine the approximate value of $\left(\frac{1}{4}\right)^{-0.5}$.**

x	y
−2	16
−1	4
0	1
1	$\frac{1}{4}$
2	$\frac{1}{16}$

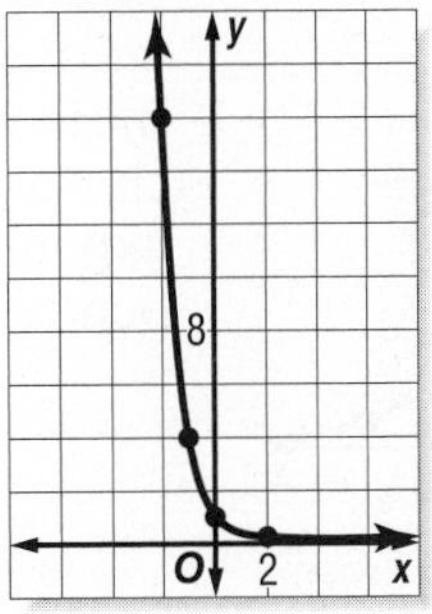

The value of $\left(\frac{1}{4}\right)^{-0.5}$ is about 2.

Exercises

1. Graph $y = 0.3^x$. State the y-intercept. Then use the graph to determine the approximate value of $0.3^{-1.5}$. Use a calculator to confirm the value.

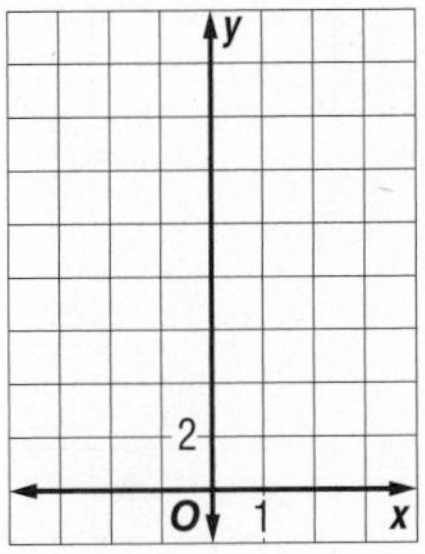

Graph each function. State the y-intercept.

2. $y = 3^x + 1$

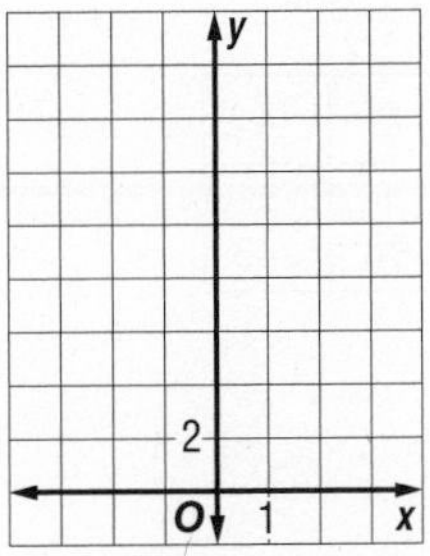

3. $y = \left(\frac{1}{3}\right)^x + 1$

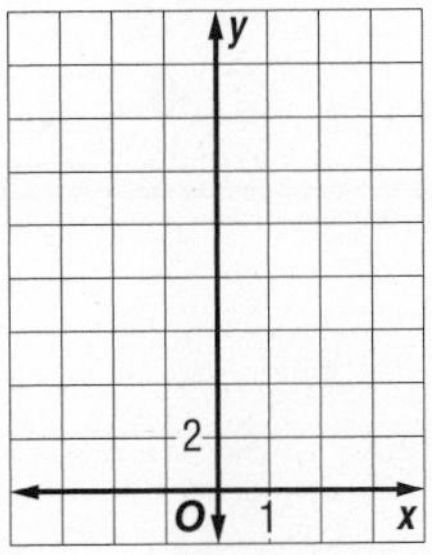

4. $y = \left(\frac{1}{2}\right)^x - 2$

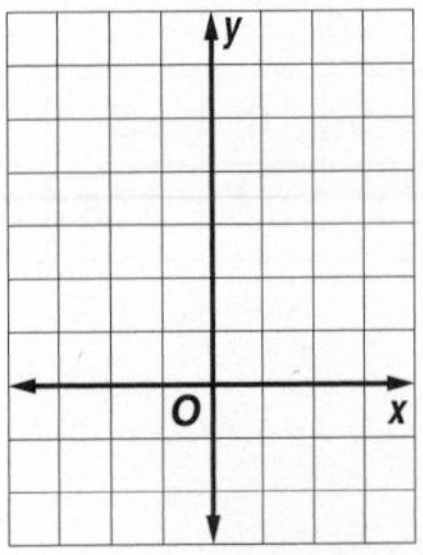

10-5 Study Guide and Intervention *(continued)*

Exponential Functions

Identify Exponential Behavior It is sometimes useful to know if a set of data is exponential. One way to tell is to observe the shape of the graph. Another way is to observe the pattern in the set of data.

Example **Determine whether the set of data displays exponential behavior.**

x	0	2	4	6	8	10
y	64	32	16	8	4	2

Method 1: Graph the Data

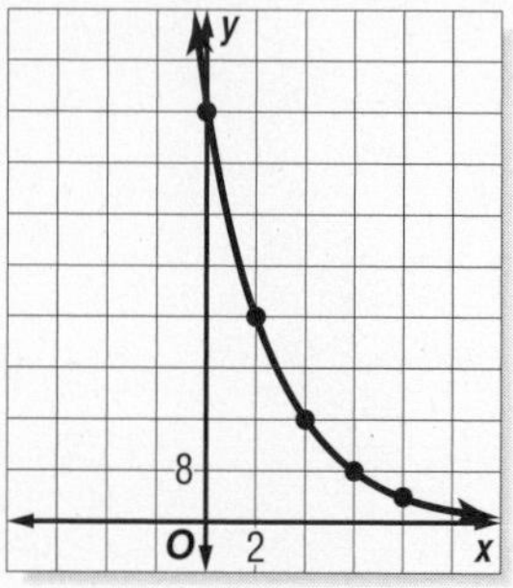

The graph shows rapidly decreasing values of y as x increases. This is characteristic of exponential behavior.

Method 2: Look for a Pattern

The domain values increase by regular intervals of 2, while the range values have a common factor of $\frac{1}{2}$. Since the domain values increase by regular intervals and the range values have a common factor, the data are probably exponential.

Exercises

Determine whether the data in each table display exponential behavior. Explain why or why not.

1.

x	0	1	2	3
y	5	10	15	20

2.

x	0	1	2	3
y	3	9	27	81

3.

x	−1	1	3	5
y	32	16	8	4

4.

x	−1	0	1	2	3
y	3	3	3	3	3

5.

x	−5	0	5	10
y	1	0.5	0.25	0.125

6.

x	0	1	2	3	4
y	$\frac{1}{3}$	$\frac{1}{9}$	$\frac{1}{27}$	$\frac{1}{81}$	$\frac{1}{243}$

NAME ______________________ DATE ____________ PERIOD _____

10-5 Skills Practice

Exponential Functions

Graph each function. State the y-intercept. Then use the graph to determine the approximate value of the given expression. Use a calculator to confirm the value.

1. $y = 2^x$; $2^{2.3}$

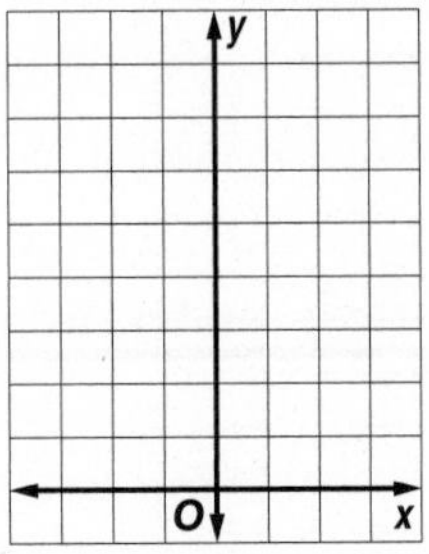

2. $y = \left(\frac{1}{3}\right)^x$; $\left(\frac{1}{3}\right)^{-1.6}$

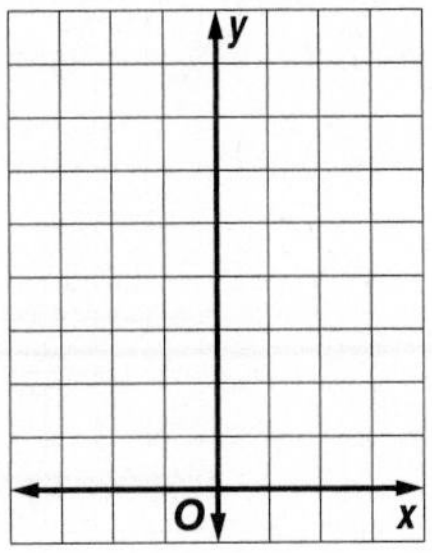

Graph each function. State the y-intercept.

3. $y = 3(2^x)$

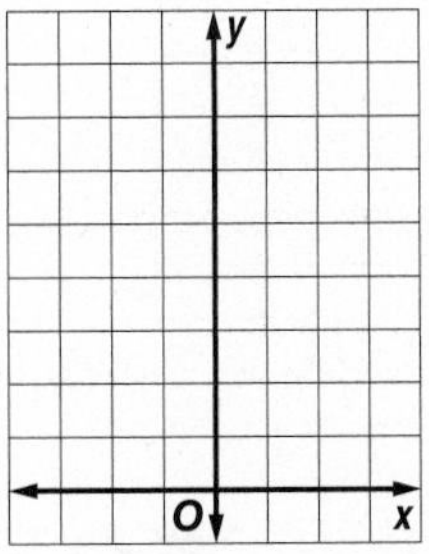

4. $y = 3^x + 2$

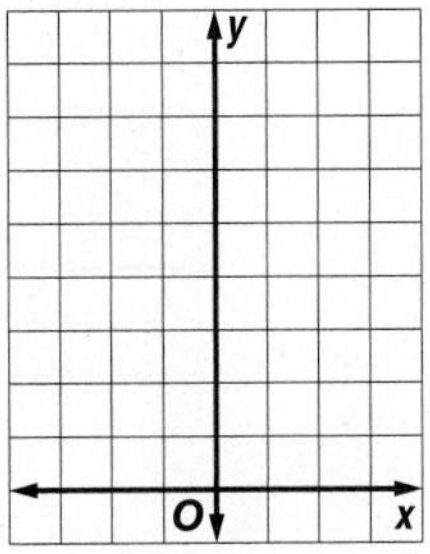

Determine whether the data in each table display exponential behavior. Explain why or why not.

5.

x	−3	−2	−1	0
y	9	12	15	18

6.

x	0	5	10	15
y	20	10	5	2.5

7.

x	4	8	12	16
y	20	40	80	160

8.

x	50	30	10	−10
y	90	70	50	30

NAME ______________________ DATE __________ PERIOD _____

10-5 Practice

Exponential Functions

Graph each function. State the *y*-intercept. Then use the graph to determine the approximate value of the given expression. Use a calculator to confirm the value.

1. $y = \left(\frac{1}{10}\right)^x; \left(\frac{1}{10}\right)^{-0.5}$

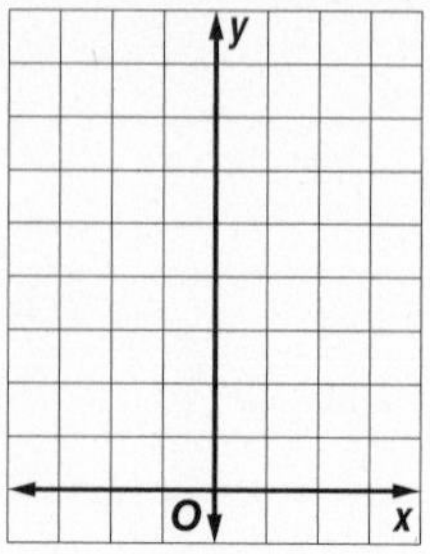

2. $y = 3^x; 3^{1.9}$

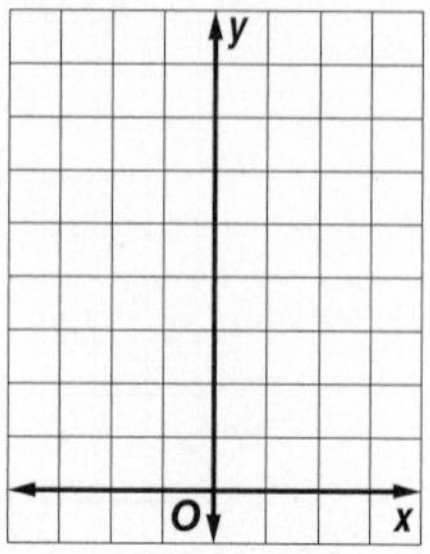

3. $y = \left(\frac{1}{4}\right)^x; \left(\frac{1}{4}\right)^{-1.4}$

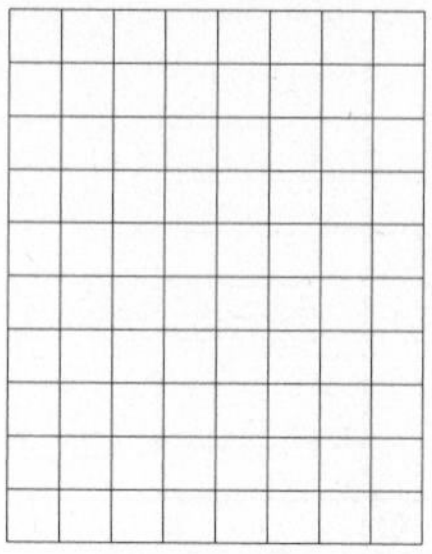

Graph each function. State the *y*-intercept.

4. $y = 4(2^x) + 1$

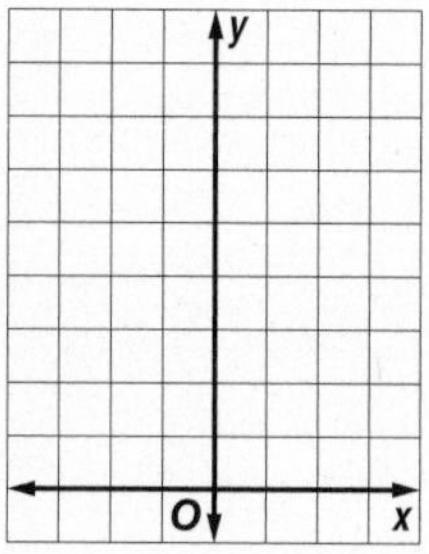

5. $y = 2(2^x - 1)$

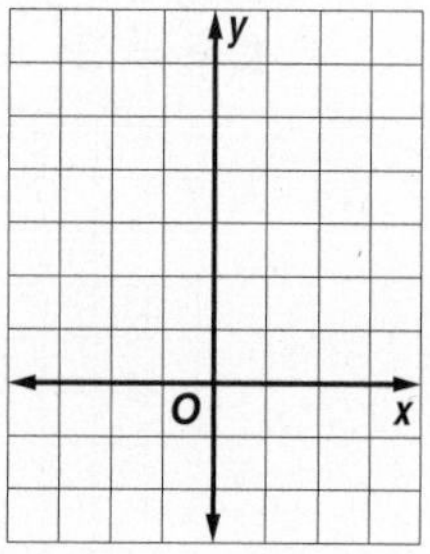

6. $y = 0.5(3^x - 3)$

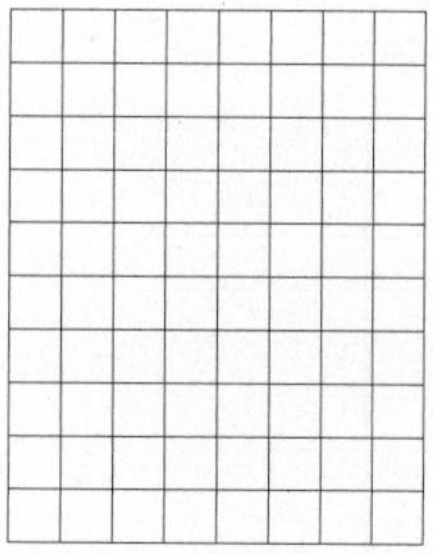

Determine whether the data in each table display exponential behavior. Explain why or why not.

7.

x	2	5	8	11
y	480	120	30	7.5

8.

x	21	18	15	12
y	30	23	16	9

9. LEARNING Ms. Klemperer told her English class that each week students tend to forget one sixth of the vocabulary words they learned the previous week. Suppose a student learns 60 words. The number of words remembered can be described by the function $W(x) = 60\left(\frac{5}{6}\right)^x$, where x is the number of weeks that pass. How many words will the student remember after 3 weeks?

10. BIOLOGY Suppose a certain cell reproduces itself in four hours. If a lab researcher begins with 50 cells, how many cells will there be after one day, two days, and three days? (*Hint:* Use the exponential function $y = 50(2^x)$.)

NAME ______________________ DATE __________ PERIOD _____

10-5 Reading to Learn Mathematics

Exponential Functions

Pre-Activity **How can exponential functions be used in art?**

Read the introduction to Lesson 10-5 at the top of page 554 in your textbook.

If Mr. Warther had carved a ninth layer of pliers, how many pliers would he have carved?

Reading the Lesson

1. The graphs of two exponential functions of the form $y = a^x$ are shown below.

A.

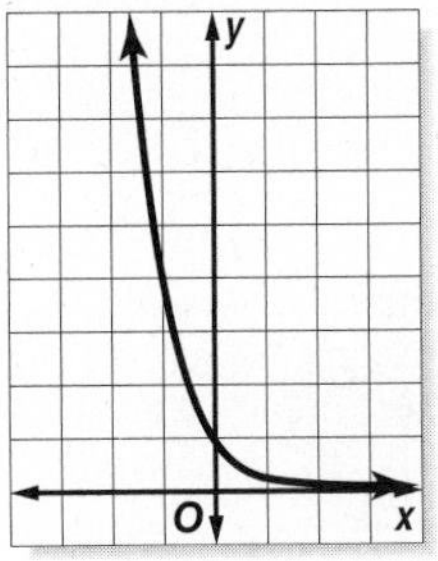

B.

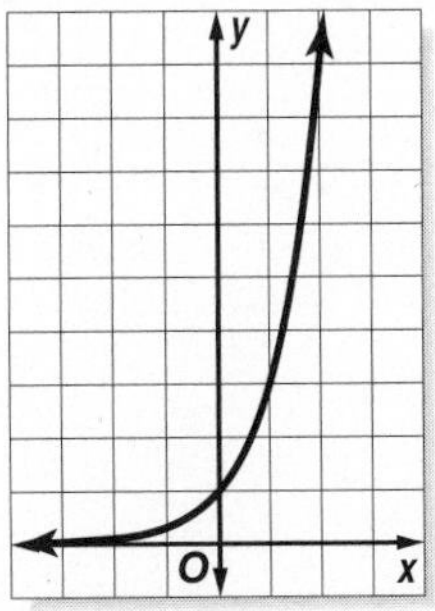

a. In Graph A, the value of a is greater than ________ and less than ________. The y values decrease as the x values ________________.

b. In Graph B, the value of a is greater than ________. The y values ________________ as the x values increase.

2. a. When you look for a pattern of exponential behavior in a set of data, what is the pattern you are looking for?

b. If a set of data has a negative common factor, does it display exponential behavior?

Helping You Remember

3. What comparisons can you make between the quadratic function $y = x^2$ and the exponential function $y = 2^x$ to help remember the differences between quadratic and exponential functions?

Lesson 10-5

NAME ______________________________ DATE ____________ PERIOD _____

10-5 Enrichment

Writing Expressions of Area in Factored Form

Write an expression in factored form for the area A of the shaded region in each figure below.

1. 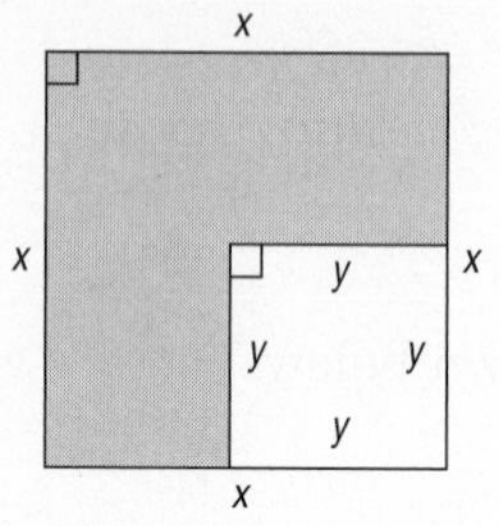

2. 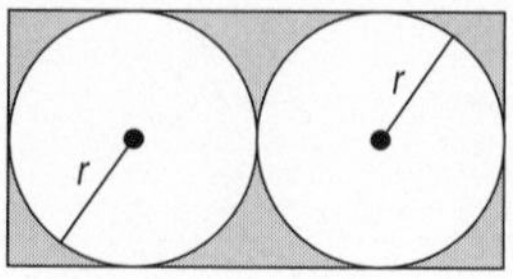

3. 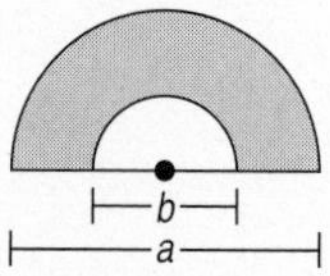

4. 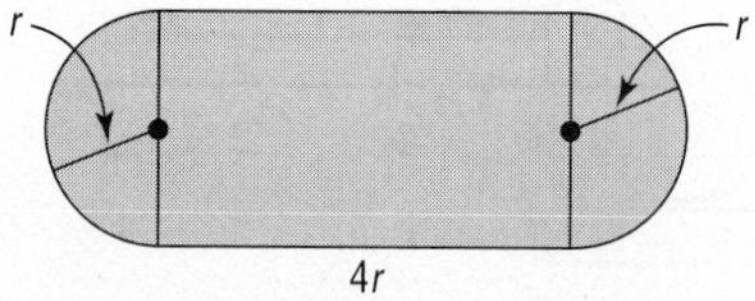

5. 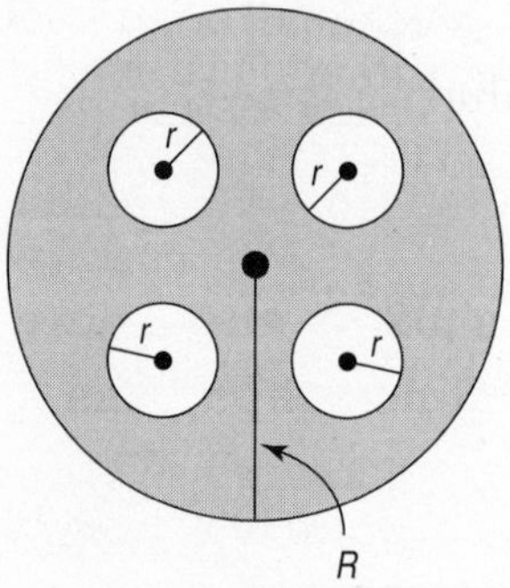

6. 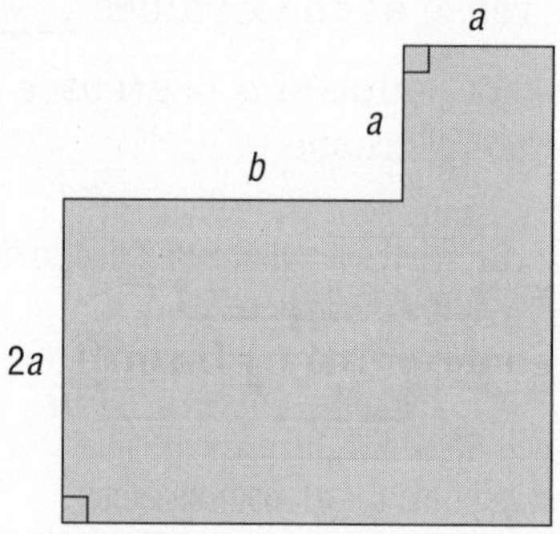

7. 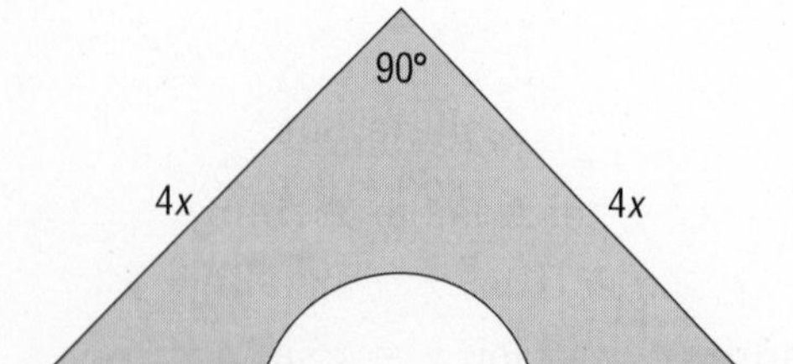

8. 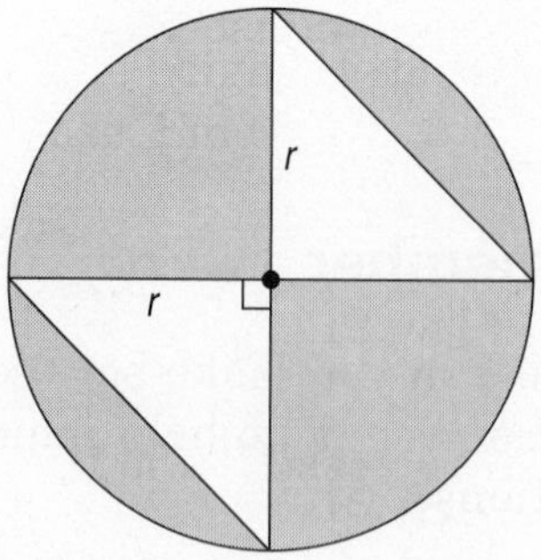

10-6 Study Guide and Intervention

Growth and Decay

Exponential Growth Population increases and growth of monetary investments are examples of **exponential growth**. This means that an initial amount increases at a steady rate over time.

Exponential Growth	The general equation for exponential growth is $y = C(1 + r)^t$. • y represents the final amount. • C represents the initial amount. • r represents the rate of change expressed as a decimal. • t represents time.

Example 1 **POPULATION The population of Johnson City in 1995 was 25,000. Since then, the population has grown at an average rate of 3.2% each year.**

a. Write an equation to represent the population of Johnson City since 1995.

The rate 3.2% can be written as 0.032.

$y = C(1 + r)^t$
$y = 25{,}000(1 + 0.032)^t$
$y = 25{,}000(1.032)^t$

b. According to the equation, what will the population of Johnson City be in the year 2005?

In 2005, t will equal 2005 − 1995 or 10.

Substitute 10 for t in the equation from part a.

$y = 25{,}000(1.032)^{10}$ $t = 10$
$\approx 34{,}256$

In 2005, the population of Johnson City will be about 34,256.

Example 2 **INVESTMENT The Garcias have $12,000 in a savings account. The bank pays 3.5% interest on savings accounts, compounded monthly. Find the balance in 3 years.**

The rate 3.5% can be written as 0.035.

The special equation for compound interest is $A = P\left(1 + \frac{r}{n}\right)^{nt}$, where A represents the balance, P is the initial amount, r represents the annual rate expressed as a decimal, n represents the number of times the interest is compounded each year, and t represents the number of years the money is invested.

$A = P\left(1 + \frac{r}{n}\right)^{nt}$

$A = 12{,}000\left(1 + \frac{0.035}{12}\right)^{36}$

$A \approx 12{,}000(1.00292)^{36}$

$A \approx 13{,}328.09$

In three years, the balance of the account will be $13,328.09.

Exercises

1. **POPULATION** The population of the United States has been increasing at an average annual rate of 0.91%. If the population of the United States was about 284,905,400 in the year 2001, predict the U. S. population in the year 2005. **Source:** U. S. Census Bureau

2. **INVESTMENT** Determine the amount of an investment of $2500 if it is invested at in interest rate of 5.25% compounded monthly for 4 years.

3. **POPULATION** It is estimated that the population of the world is increasing at an average annual rate of 1.3%. If the population of the world was about 6,167,007,000 in the year 2001, predict the world population in the year 2010. **Source:** U. S. Census Bureau

4. **INVESTMENT** Determine the amount of an investment of $100,000 if it is invested at an interest rate of 5.2% compounded quarterly for 12 years.

10-6 Study Guide and Intervention *(continued)*

Growth and Decay

Exponential Decay Radioactive decay and depreciation are examples of **exponential decay**. This means that an initial amount decreases at a steady rate over a period of time.

Exponential Decay	The general equation for exponential decay is $y = C(1 - r)^t$. • y represents the final amount. • C represents the initial amount. • r represents the rate of decay expressed as a decimal. • t represents time.

Example **DEPRECIATION The original price of a tractor was $45,000. The value of the tractor decreases at a steady rate of 12% per year.**

a. Write an equation to represent the value of the tractor since it was purchased.

The rate 12% can be written as 0.12.

$y = C(1 - r)^t$ General equation for exponential decay

$y = 45{,}000(1 - 0.12)^t$ $C = 45{,}000$ and $r = 0.12$

$y = 45{,}000(0.88)^t$ Simplify.

b. What is the value of the tractor in 5 years?

$y = 45{,}000(0.88)^t$ Equation for decay from part a

$y = 45{,}000(0.88)^5$ $t = 5$

$y \approx 23{,}747.94$ Use a calculator.

In 5 years, the tractor will be worth about $23,747.94.

Exercises

1. **POPULATION** The population of Bulgaria has been decreasing at an annual rate of 1.3%. If the population of Bulgaria was about 7,797,000 in the year 2000, predict its population in the year 2010. **Source:** U. S. Census Bureau

2. **DEPRECIATION** Carl Gossell is a machinist. He bought some new machinery for about $125,000. He wants to calculate the value of the machinery over the next 10 years for tax purposes. If the machinery depreciates at the rate of 15% per year, what is the value of the machinery (to the nearest $100) at the end of 10 years?

3. **ARCHAEOLOGY** The *half-life* of a radioactive element is defined as the time that it takes for one-half a quantity of the element to decay. Radioactive Carbon-14 is found in all living organisms and has a half-life of 5730 years. Consider a living organism with an original concentration of Carbon-14 of 100 grams.
   a. If the organism lived 5730 years ago, what is the concentration of Carbon-14 today?
   b. If the organism lived 11,460 years ago, determine the concentration of Carbon-14 today.

4. **DEPRECIATION** A new car costs $32,000. It is expected to depreciate 12% each year for 4 years and then depreciate 8% each year thereafter. Find the value of the car in 6 years.

10-6 Skills Practice

Growth and Decay

POPULATION For Exercises 1 and 2, use the following information.

The population of New York City increased from 7,322,564 in 1990 to 8,008,278 in 2000. The annual rate of population increase for the period was about 0.9%. **Source:** www.nyc.gov

1. Write an equation for the population t years after 1990.

2. Use the equation to predict the population of New York City in 2010.

SAVINGS For Exercises 3 and 4, use the following information.

The Fresh and Green Company has a savings plan for its employees. If an employee makes an initial contribution of $1000, the company pays 8% interest compounded quarterly.

3. If an employee participating in the plan withdraws the balance of the account after 5 years, how much will be in the account?

4. If an employee participating in the plan withdraws the balance of the account after 35 years, how much will be in the account?

5. HOUSING Mr. and Mrs. Boyce bought a house for $96,000 in 1995. The real estate broker indicated that houses in their area are appreciating at an average annual rate of 4%. If the appreciation remains steady at this rate, what will be the value of the Boyce's home in 2005?

MANUFACTURING For Exercises 6 and 7, use the following information.

Zeller Industries bought a piece of weaving equipment for $60,000. It is expected to depreciate at an average rate of 10% per year.

6. Write an equation for the value of the piece of equipment after t years.

7. Find the value of the piece of equipment after 6 years.

8. FINANCES Kyle saved $500 from a summer job. He plans to spend 10% of his savings each week on various forms of entertainment. At this rate, how much will Kyle have left after 15 weeks?

9. TRANSPORTATION Tiffany's mother bought a car for $9000 five years ago. She wants to sell it to Tiffany based on a 15% annual rate of depreciation. At this rate, how much will Tiffany pay for the car?

10-6 Practice

Growth and Decay

COMMUNICATIONS For Exercises 1 and 2, use the following information.

Commercial non-music radio stations increased at an average annual rate of 3.1% from 1996 to 2000. Commercial radio stations in this format numbered 1262 in 1996.

Source: M Street Corporation, Nashville, TN

1. Write an equation for the number of radio stations for t years after 1996.

2. If the trend continues, predict the number of radio stations in this format for the year 2006.

3. **INVESTMENTS** Determine the amount of an investment if \$500 is invested at an interest rate of 4.25% compounded quarterly for 12 years.

4. **INVESTMENTS** Determine the amount of an investment if \$300 is invested at an interest rate of 6.75% compounded semiannually for 20 years.

5. **HOUSING** The Greens bought a condominium for \$110,000 in 2000. If its value appreciates at an average rate of 6% per year, what will the value be in 2005?

DEFORESTATION For Exercises 6 and 7, use the following information.

During the 1990s, the forested area of Guatemala decreased at an average rate of 1.7%.

Source: www.worldbank.org

6. If the forested area in Guatemala in 1990 was about 34,400 square kilometers, write an equation for the forested area for t years after 1990.

7. If this trend continues, predict the forested area in 2015.

8. **BUSINESS** A piece of machinery valued at \$25,000 depreciates at a steady rate of 10% yearly. What will the value of the piece of machinery be after 7 years?

9. **TRANSPORTATION** A new car costs \$18,000. It is expected to depreciate at an average rate of 12% per year. Find the value of the car in 8 years.

10. **POPULATION** The population of Osaka, Japan declined at an average annual rate of 0.05% for the five years between 1995 and 2000. If the population of Osaka was 11,013,000 in 2000 and it continues to decline at the same rate, predict the population in 2050.

NAME ______________________________ DATE ____________ PERIOD _____

10-6 Reading to Learn Mathematics

Growth and Decay

Lesson 10-6

Pre-Activity **How can exponential growth be used to predict future sales?**

Read the introduction to Lesson 10-6 at the top of page 561 in your textbook.

Suppose you want to predict the amount of money an average household will spend on restaurant meals in the year 2005. What number should be substituted for t?

Reading the Lesson

Match an equation to each situation, and then indicate whether the situation is an example of exponential growth or decay.

1. A coin had a value of \$1.17 in 1995. Its value has been increasing at a rate of 9% per year.

A. $y = 1.17(1.09)^t$ **B.** $y = 1.17(0.91)^t$

2. A business owner has just paid \$6000 for a computer. It depreciates at a rate of 22% per year. How much will it be worth in 5 years?

A. $A = 6000(1.22)^5$ **B.** $A = 6000(0.78)^5$

3. A city had a population of 14,358 residents in 1999. Since then, its population has been decreasing at a rate of about 5.5% per year.

A. $A = 14{,}358(1.055)^t$ **B.** $A = 14{,}358(0.945)^t$

4. Gina deposited \$1500 in an account that pays 4% interest compounded quarterly. What will be the worth of the account in 2 years if she makes no deposits and no withdrawals?

A. $A = 1500(1.02)^2$ **B.** $A = 1500(1.02)^8$

Helping You Remember

5. How can you use what you know about raising a number to the 0 power to help you remember what C represents in the exponential growth equation $A = C(1 + r)^t$ and the exponential decay equation $A = C(1 - r)^t$?

NAME ________________ DATE ________ PERIOD _____

10-6 Enrichment

Curious Circles

Two circles can be arranged in four ways: one circle can be inside the other, they can be separate, they can overlap, or they can coincide.

In how many ways can a given number of circles be either separate or inside each other? (The situations in which the circles overlap or coincide are not counted here.)

For 3 circles, there are 4 different possibilities.

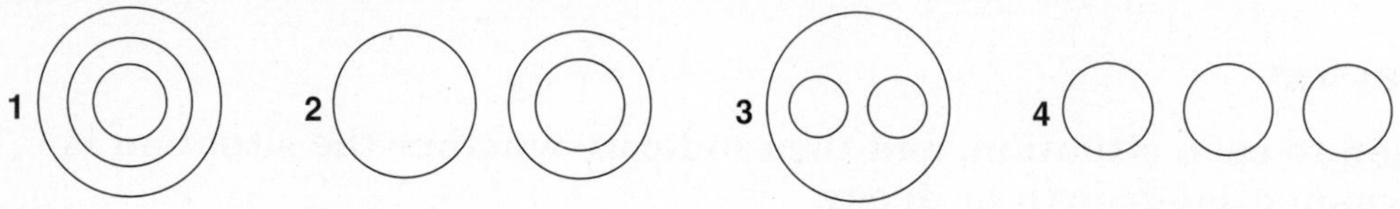

Solve each problem. Make drawings to show your answers.

1. Show the different ways in which 2 circles can be separate or inside each other. How many ways are there?

2. Show the different ways for 4 circles. How many ways are there?

3. Use your answer for Exercise 2 to show that the number of ways for 5 circles is at least 18.

4. Find the number of ways for 5 circles. Show your drawings on a separate sheet of paper.

10-7 Study Guide and Intervention

Geometric Sequences

Geometric Sequences A **geometric sequence** is a sequence in which each term after the nonzero first term is found by multiplying the previous term by a constant called the **common ratio**.

Geometric Sequence	a sequence of numbers of the form $a, ar, ar^2, ar^3, \ldots$, where $a \neq 0$, and $r \neq 0$ or 1	**Example:** 1, 2, 4, 8, 16, …

Example 1 **Determine whether each sequence is geometric.**

a. 3, 6, 9, 12, 15, ...

In this sequence, each term is found by adding 3 to the previous term. The sequence is arithmetic and not geometric.

b. 1, 4, 16, 64, ...

In this sequence, each term is found by multiplying the previous term by 4. The sequence is geometric.

Example 2 **Find the next three terms in each geometric sequence.**

a. 8, −4, 2, −1, ...

The common factor is $\frac{-4}{8}$ or $-\frac{1}{2}$. Use this information to find the next three terms.

$(-1)\left(-\frac{1}{2}\right) = \frac{1}{2}$

$\frac{1}{2}\left(-\frac{1}{2}\right) = -\frac{1}{4}$

$\left(-\frac{1}{4}\right)\left(-\frac{1}{2}\right) = \frac{1}{8}$

The next three terms are $\frac{1}{2}$, $-\frac{1}{4}$, and $\frac{1}{8}$.

b. 7, 14, 28, 56, ...

The common ratio is $\frac{14}{7}$ or 2. Use this information to find the next three terms.

$56(2) = 112$

$112(2) = 224$

$224(2) = 448$

The next three terms are 112, 224, 448.

Exercises

Determine whether each sequence is geometric.

1. 2, 4, 6, 8, 10, …

2. 2, 4, 8, 16, 32, …

3. −10, −5, −2.5, −1.25, …

4. 100, 400, 1600, 6400, …

5. $\frac{1}{2}, \frac{1}{3}, \frac{1}{4}, \frac{1}{5}, \ldots$

6. $\frac{1}{3}, \frac{1}{9}, \frac{1}{27}, \frac{1}{81}, \ldots$

Find the next three terms in each geometric sequence.

7. 100, 300, 900, 2700, …

8. $\frac{1}{2}, \frac{1}{4}, \frac{1}{8}, \frac{1}{16}, \ldots$

9. 80, 40, 20, 10, …

Find the *n*th term of each geometric sequence.

10. $a_1 = 5, n = 6, r = 3$

11. $a_1 = 3, n = 5, r = 4$

12. $a_1 = -5, n = 7, r = -2$

10-7 Study Guide and Intervention *(continued)*

Geometric Sequences

Geometric Means A missing term or terms between two nonconsecutive terms in a geometric sequence are called **geometric means**. In the sequence 10, 20, 40, 80, …, the geometric mean between 10 and 40 is 20. You can use the formula $a_n = a_1 \cdot r^{n-1}$ to find a geometric mean.

Example **Find the geometric mean in the sequence 6, ___, 150.**

In the sequence, $a_1 = 6$ and $a_3 = 150$. To find a_2, you must first find r.

$a_n = a_1 \cdot r^{n-1}$	Formula for the *n*th term of a geometric sequence
$a_3 = a_1 \cdot r^{3-1}$	$n = 3$
$150 = 6 \cdot r^2$	$a_3 = 150$ and $a_1 = 6$
$\frac{150}{6} = \frac{6r^2}{6}$	Divide each side by 6.
$25 = r^2$	Simplify.
$\pm 5 = r$	Take the square root of each side.

If $r = 5$, the geometric mean is 6(5) or 30. If $r = -5$, the geometric mean is $6(-5)$ or -30. Therefore the geometric mean is 30 or -30.

Exercises

Find the geometric means in each sequence.

1. 4, ___, 16

2. 12, ___, 108

3. -8, ___, -128

4. 180, ___, 20

5. -2, ___, -98

6. 600, ___, 150

7. $\frac{1}{4}$, ___, $\frac{1}{16}$

8. $\frac{1}{2}$, ___, $\frac{1}{32}$

9. $-\frac{3}{5}$, ___, $-\frac{15}{16}$

10. 14, ___, $\frac{2}{7}$

11. $\frac{5}{8}$, ___, 10

12. $-\frac{2}{3}$, ___, -54

13. 2.3, ___, 9.2

14. -137.7, ___, -15.3

15. -5.1, ___, -127.5

16. $\frac{3}{8}$, ___, $\frac{3}{32}$

17. -15, ___, $-\frac{3}{5}$

18. 8, ___, 320,000

NAME ______________________ DATE ____________ PERIOD _____

10-7 Skills Practice

Geometric Sequences

Determine whether each sequence is geometric.

1. 9, 17, 25, 33, ...

2. 4, 12, 36, 108, ...

3. $-320, -80, -20, -5, \ldots$

4. $-75, -60, -45, -30, \ldots$

5. $64, -32, 16, -8, \ldots$

6. 26.5, 21, 15.5, 10, ...

Find the next three terms in each geometric sequence.

7. $2, -4, 8, -16, \ldots$

8. $-2, -6, -18, -54, \ldots$

9. $-960, 480, -240, 120, \ldots$

10. 7290, 2430, 810, 270, ...

11. $-32, -16, -8, -4, \ldots$

12. 6144, 1536, 384, 96, ...

Find the *n*th term of each geometric sequence.

13. $a_1 = 2, n = 4, r = -2$

14. $a_1 = 3, n = 5, r = 2$

15. $a_1 = 6, n = 3, r = 8$

16. $a_1 = -5, n = 4, r = 9$

17. $a_1 = 10, n = 3, r = 12$

18. $a_1 = 4, n = 4, r = -8$

Find the geometric means in each sequence.

19. 8, ___, 72

20. 75, ___, 3

21. -2, ___, -128

22. -112, ___, -7

23. 324, ___, 4

24. 1.5, ___, 24

Lesson 10-7

NAME ______________________________ DATE ____________ PERIOD _____

10-7 Practice

Geometric Sequences

Determine whether each sequence is geometric.

1. 3, 12, 48, 192, ...

2. 2, 17, 32, 47, ...

3. $-200, -135, -70, -5, \ldots$

4. $-220, -110, -55, -27.5, \ldots$

5. $-992, 248, -62, 15.5, \ldots$

6. $-20, -50, -125, -312.5, \ldots$

Find the next three terms in each geometric sequence.

7. $-4, -20, -100, -500, \ldots$

8. $7, -21, 63, -189, \ldots$

9. $-6250, 1250, -250, 50 \ldots$

10. 50, 70, 98, 137.2, ...

11. $5, -4, 3.2, -2.56 \ldots$

12. $\frac{1}{4}, \frac{1}{6}, \frac{1}{9}, \frac{2}{27}, \ldots$

Find the *n*th term of each geometric sequence.

13. $a_1 = 6, n = 5, r = 3$

14. $a_1 = -9, n = 6, r = 2$

15. $a_1 = 8, n = 3, r = -11$

16. $a_1 = 50, n = 7, r = 3$

17. $a_1 = -5, n = 3, r = 1.5$

18. $a_1 = 7, n = 5, r = 0.5$

Find the geometric means in each sequence.

19. 4, ___, 256

20. -8, ___, -392

21. 2, ___, 0.5

22. -20, ___, -1.25

23. $\frac{3}{4}$, ___, $\frac{3}{64}$

24. $\frac{1}{2}$, ___, $\frac{2}{25}$

MAGAZINE SUBSCRIPTIONS For Exercises 25 and 26, use the following information.
The manager of a teen magazine wants to increase subscriptions by at least 6% each year for the next three years to keep the company operating at a profit. Subscriptions for 2003 are 17,500.

25. Determine the minimum number of subscriptions the sales team must sell for the years 2004, 2005, and 2006.

26. Suppose the manager wants to increase the subscriptions to 35,000. How long will it take to reach this goal if subscriptions increase at 6% per year?

10-7 Reading to Learn Mathematics

Geometric Sequences

Pre-Activity **How can a geometric sequence be used to describe a bungee jump?**

Read the introduction to Lesson 10-7 at the top of page 567 in your textbook.

How can you find the distance of the fifth bounce?

Reading the Lesson

1. Suppose you are given the first three terms of a geometric sequence and want to find the next three terms.

a. What should you do to find the common ratio?

b. What should you do after you find the common ratio?

2. Suppose you are asked to give an example of a geometric sequence. Are there any restrictions on the terms of the sequence or the common ratio r? Explain.

3. You can use the formula for the nth term of a geometric sequence to find any term in the sequence.What information do you need in order to use the formula?

4. Consider the geometric sequence 3, 6, 12, 24, 48, …. How many geometric means are there for each pair of terms? What are they?

a. 3 and 12

b. 3 and 24

Helping You Remember

5. To remember an idea, it can help if you explain it to someone else. Suppose a friend thinks that the formula for the nth term of a geometric sequence should be $a_n = a_1r^n$ rather than $a_n = a_1r^{n-1}$. How would you explain why it should be $a_n = a_1r^{n-1}$?

NAME ______________________________ DATE ____________ PERIOD _____

10-7 Enrichment

Convergence, Divergence, and Limits

Imagine that a runner runs a mile from point A to point B. But, this is not an ordinary race! In the first minute, he runs one-half mile, reaching point C. In the next minute, he covers one-half the remaining distance, or $\frac{1}{4}$ mile, reaching point D. In the next minute he covers one-half the remaining distance, or $\frac{1}{8}$ mile, reaching point E.

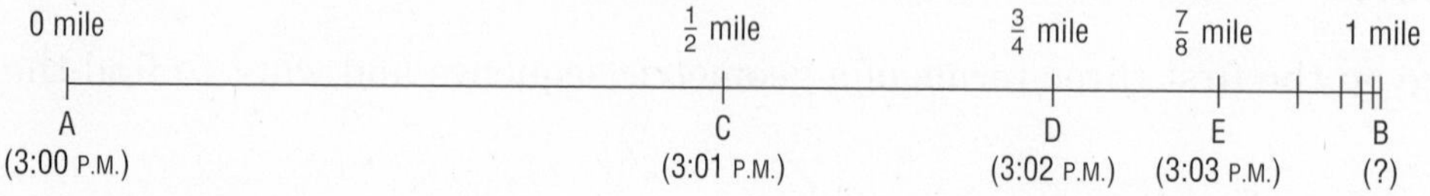

In this strange race, the runner approaches closer and closer to point B, but never gets there. However close he is to B, there is still some distance remaining, and in the next minute he can cover only half of that distance. This race can be modeled by the infinite sequence

$\frac{1}{2}, \frac{3}{4}, \frac{7}{8}, \frac{15}{16}, \ldots$

The terms of the sequence get closer and closer to 1. An infinite sequence that gets arbitrarily close to some number is said to **converge** to that number. The number is the limit of the sequence.

Not all infinite sequences converge. Those that do not are called **divergent**.

Write C if the sequence converges and D if it diverges. If the sequence converges, make a reasonable guess for its limit.

1. 2, 4, 6, 8, 10, …

2. 0, 3, 0, 3, 0, 3, …

3. $1, \frac{1}{2}, \frac{1}{3}, \frac{1}{4}, \frac{1}{5}, \ldots$

4. 0.9, 0.99, 0.999, 0.9999, …

5. $-5, 5, -5, 5, -5, 5, \ldots$

6. 0.1, 0.2, 0.3, 0.4, …

7. $2\frac{1}{4}, 2\frac{3}{4}, 2\frac{7}{8}, 2\frac{15}{16}, \ldots$

8. $6, 5\frac{1}{2}, 5\frac{1}{3}, 5\frac{1}{4}, 5\frac{1}{5}, \ldots$

9. 1, 4, 9, 16, 25, …

10. $-1, -\frac{1}{2}, -\frac{1}{3}, -\frac{1}{4}, -\frac{1}{5}, \ldots$

11. Create one convergent sequence and one divergent sequence. Give the limit for your convergent sequence.

10 Chapter 10 Test, Form 1

SCORE _____

Write the letter for the correct answer in the blank at the right of each question.

1. Which equation corresponds to the graph shown?

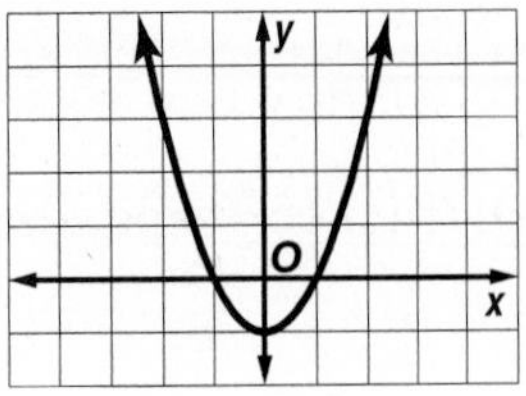

A. $y = x^2 + 1$ **B.** $y = -x^2 - 1$

C. $y = x^2 - 1$ **D.** $y = x^2$ **1.** _____

2. What is the equation of the axis of symmetry of the graph of $y = x^2 + 6x - 7$?

A. $x = 6$ **B.** $x = -3$

C. $x = 3$ **D.** $x = -6$ **2.** _____

3. Find the coordinates of the vertex of the graph of $y = 4 - x^2$. Identify the vertex as a maximum or a minimum.

A. (2, 0); maximum **B.** (0, 4); minimum

C. (0, 4); maximum **D.** (2, 0); minimum **3.** _____

4. What are the roots of the quadratic equation whose related function is graphed at the right?

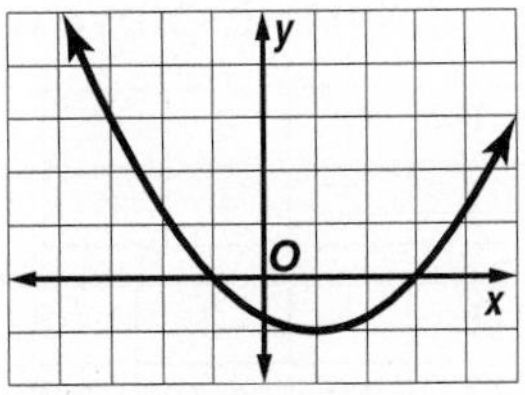

A. $-1, 3$ **B.** $-1, 1$

C. $-3, 1$ **D.** $1, 3$ **4.** _____

5. One root of the quadratic equation whose related function is graphed lies between which consecutive integers?

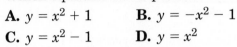

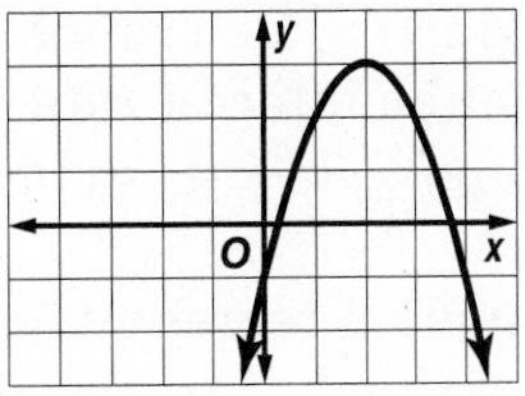

A. 1 and 2 **B.** 2 and 3

C. 0 and -1 **D.** 0 and 1 **5.** _____

6. Solve $k^2 + 4k + 4 = 25$ by taking the square root of each side.

A. $-5, 5$ **B.** 5 **C.** $-3, 7$ **D.** $-7, 3$ **6.** _____

7. Which value of c makes $y^2 + 8y + c$ a perfect square?

A. 4 **B.** 16 **C.** 64 **D.** 8 **7.** _____

8. Which equation is equivalent to $x^2 + 2x - 3 = 0$?

A. $(x + 1)^2 = 2$ **B.** $(x - 1)^2 = 4$ **C.** $(x - 1)^2 = 2$ **D.** $(x + 1)^2 = 4$ **8.** _____

9. Solve the equation $2x^2 + 3x - 5 = 0$ by using the Quadratic Formula.

A. $-2\frac{1}{2}, 1$ **B.** $-5, 1$ **C.** $-1, 2\frac{1}{2}$ **D.** $-1, 5$ **9.** _____

10. State the value of the discriminant for $y = x^2 - 8x + 10$.

A. 4.9 **B.** 24 **C.** 104 **D.** 10.2 **10.** _____

Assessment

10 Chapter 10 Test, Form 1 *(continued)*

11. Determine the number of real roots of $n^2 - 5n - 6 = 0$.

A. 1 real root **B.** 2 real roots
C. infinitely many real roots **D.** no real roots **11.** _____

12. Which equation corresponds to the graph shown?

A. $y = 2^x + 2$ **B.** $y = \left(\frac{1}{2}\right)^x - 2$

C. $y = 2^x - 2$ **D.** $y = \left(\frac{1}{2}\right)^x + 2$ **12.** _____

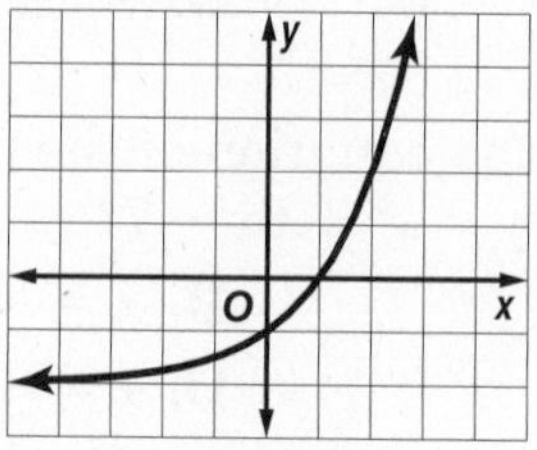

13. TOURNAMENTS A chess tournament starts with 16 people competing. The exponential function $y = 16\left(\frac{1}{2}\right)^x$ describes how many people are remaining in the tournament after x rounds. How many people are left in the tournament after 2 rounds?

A. 4 **B.** 2 **C.** 8 **D.** 1 **13.** _____

14. Which set of data displays exponential behavior?

A.

x	0	1	2	3
y	0	2	4	6

B.

x	0	1	2	3
y	0	1	16	81

C.

x	0	1	2	3
y	1	10	100	1,000

D.

x	0	1	2	3
y	6	4	2	1

14. _____

15. INVESTMENTS Determine the amount of an investment if \$1000 is invested at an interest rate of 8% compounded quarterly for 2 years.

A. \$1160.00 **B.** \$1171.66 **C.** \$1040.40 **D.** \$1166.40 **15.** _____

16. Which equation represents exponential decay?

A. $y = 0.5(1.2)^x$ **B.** $y = 10(1.1)^x$ **C.** $y = 100(0.9)^x$ **D.** $y = 0.1x^2$ **16.** _____

17. BIOLOGY If $y = 10(2.5)^t$ represents the number of bacteria in a culture at time t, how many will there be at time $t = 6$?

A. 2441 **B.** 244 **C.** 24 **D.** none **17.** _____

18. Determine which sequence is geometric.

A. 5, 11, 17, 23, ... **B.** 4, −5, −14, −23, ...
C. 19, 2, 17, 4, ... **D.** 2, 6, 18, 54, ... **18.** _____

19. Find the next three terms in the geometric sequence 5, 10, 20, 40, ...

A. 100, 180, 280 **B.** 80, 160, 320 **C.** 60, 100, 160 **D.** 60, 80, 100 **19.** _____

20. Find the geometric mean in the sequence 6, _____, 24.

A. 15 or −15 **B.** 9 or −9 **C.** 12 or −12 **D.** 18 or −18 **20.** _____

Bonus If $b^2 - 4ac = 0$, determine the number of real roots of the equation $ax^2 + bx + c = 0$. **B:** ____________

NAME ______________________ DATE ____________ PERIOD ________

Chapter 10 Test, Form 2A

SCORE ________

Write the letter for the correct answer in the blank at the right of each question.

1. Which equation corresponds to the graph shown?

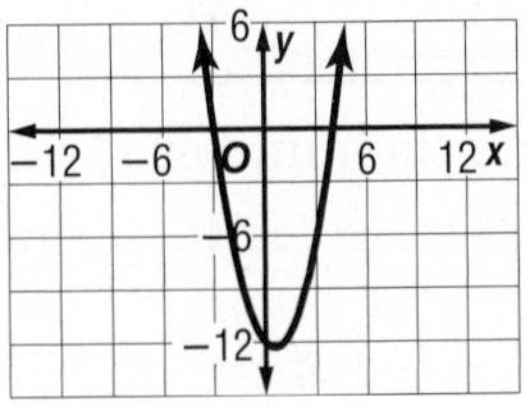

A. $y = x^2 - 7x - 12$
B. $y = x^2 - x - 12$
C. $y = x^2 + 5x + 12$
D. $y = x^2 + 12x - 1$

1. ________

2. Find the equation of the axis of symmetry and the coordinates of the vertex of the graph of $y = 2x^2 - 12x + 6$.

A. $x = -3$; $(-3, 60)$ **B.** $x = 3$; $(3, -12)$
C. $x = -3$; $(-3, 78)$ **D.** $x = 3$; $(3, 6)$

2. ________

3. Find the coordinates of the vertex of the graph of $y = -2x^2 - 8$. Identify the vertex as a maximum or a minimum.

A. $(-2, -16)$; minimum **B.** $(-2, 8)$; maximum
C. $(2, -16)$; maximum **D.** $(0, -8)$; maximum

3. ________

4. What are the root(s) of the quadratic equation whose related function is graphed at the right?

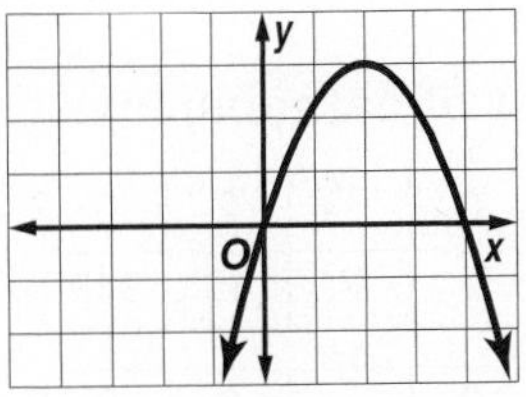

A. 2 **B.** 3
C. 0, 4 **D.** −4, 0

4. ________

5. One root of the quadratic equation whose related function is graphed lies between which consecutive integers?

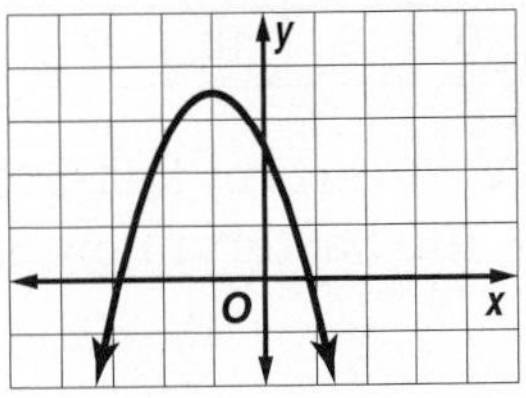

A. −3 and −2 **B.** 2 and 3
C. −2 and −1 **D.** 1 and 2

5. ________

6. Solve $a^2 - 22a + 121 = 16$ by taking the square root of each side.

A. 4 **B.** 7, 15 **C.** ±4 **D.** −15, −7

6. ________

7. Which step is *not* performed in the process of solving $n^2 - 12n - 10 = 0$ by completing the square?

A. Add 10 to each side. **B.** Add 36 to each side.
C. Factor $n^2 - 12n - 10 = 0$. **D.** Take the square root of each side.

7. ________

8. Which equation is equivalent to $2x^2 - 24x - 14 = 0$?

A. $(x - 6)^2 = 50$ **B.** $(x - 3)^2 = 13$ **C.** $(x - 3)^2 = 20$ **D.** $(x - 6)^2 = 43$

8. ________

For Questions 9 and 10, solve each equation by using the Quadratic Formula. Round to the nearest tenth if necessary.

9. $4x^2 + 11x - 3 = 0$

A. −2.4, −0.3 **B.** $-\frac{1}{4}, 3$ **C.** 0.3, 2.4 **D.** $-3, \frac{1}{4}$

9. ________

NAME ______________________________ DATE ____________ PERIOD _____

10 Chapter 10 Test, Form 2A *(continued)*

10. $y^2 + 8y = 2$

A. −8.2, 0.2 **B.** 8.2, −0.2 **C.** 0.3, 7.7 **D.** −7.7, −0.3 **10.** _____

11. Determine the number of real roots of $7x^2 - 18x + 12$.

A. 2 **B.** infinitely many **C.** none **D.** 1 **11.** _____

12. State the value of the discriminant for $4x^2 + 5x = 6$.

A. 121 **B.** 101 **C.** −71 **D.** 11 **12.** _____

13. Which equation corresponds to the graph shown?

A. $y = (3)^x + 1$ **B.** $y = 2(3^x + 1)$

C. $y = 2(3^x)$ **D.** $y = (2 \cdot 3)^x + 1$ **13.** _____

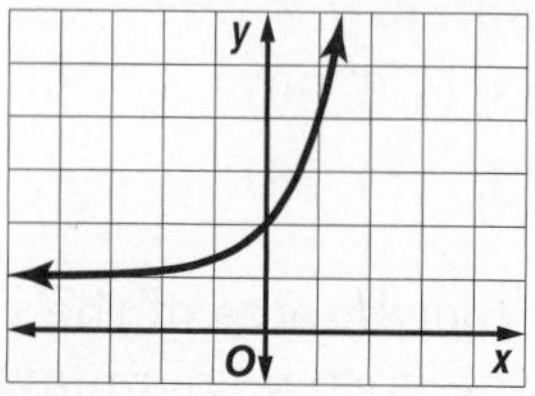

14. A weight lifter can deadlift 315 pounds. She can increase the weight $W(x)$ that she can lift according to the function $W(x) = 315(1.05)^x$, where x represents the number of training cycles completed. How much will she deadlift after 4 training cycles?

A. 365 lb **B.** 383 lb **C.** 378 lb **D.** 402 lb **14.** _____

15. Which set of data displays exponential behavior?

A.

x	0	1	2	3
y	1	7	49	343

B.

x	0	1	2	3
y	0	1	4	27

C.

x	0	1	2	3
y	0	9	18	27

D.

x	0	1	2	3
y	24	12	6	1

15. _____

16. **BIOLOGY** A certain fast-growing bacteria increases 6% per minute. If there are 100 bacteria now, about how many will there be 12 minutes later?

A. 172 **B.** 201 **C.** 48 **D.** 190 **16.** _____

17. **POPULATION** A city's population is about 954,000 and is decreasing at an annual rate of 0.1%. Predict the population in 50 years.

A. 577,176 **B.** 906,300 **C.** 1,002,888 **D.** 907,450 **17.** _____

18. Determine which sequence is geometric.

A. −16, −13, −10, −7, ... **B.** 1, 1, 2, 3, 5, ...

C. −3, −6, −12, −24, ... **D.** 5, 7, 9, 11, ... **18.** _____

19. Find the fifth term in a geometric sequence in which $a_1 = 3$ and $r = -4$.

A. 60 **B.** −3072 **C.** −729 **D.** 768 **19.** _____

20. Find the geometric mean in the sequence −48, ____, −768.

A. 408 or −408 **B.** 192 or −192 **C.** 204 or −204 **D.** 328 or −328 **20.** _____

Bonus What is the equation of the axis of symmetry of a parabola if its x-intercepts are −3 and 5? **B:** ______________

NAME ______________________ DATE ____________ PERIOD ________

10 Chapter 10 Test, Form 2B

SCORE ________

Write the letter for the correct answer in the blank at the right of each question.

1. Which equation corresponds to the graph shown?

A. $y = x^2 - 3x - 10$
B. $y = x^2 + 7x + 10$
C. $y = x^2 - 10x + 6$
D. $y = x^2 - 11x - 10$

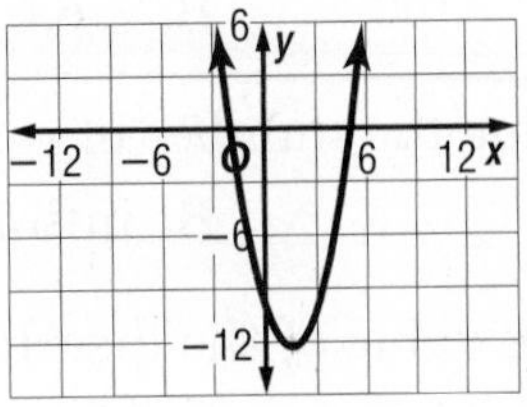

1. ______

2. Find the equation of the axis of symmetry and the coordinates of the vertex of the graph of $y = -x^2 - 10x + 17$.

A. $x = -5; (-5, -8)$ **B.** $x = -5; (-5, 42)$
C. $x = 5; (5, 92)$ **D.** $x = 5; (5, 32)$

2. ______

3. Find the coordinates of the vertex of the graph of $y = 3x^2 - 6$. Identify the vertex as a maximum or a minimum.

A. $(0, -6)$; maximum **B.** $(-6, 0)$; minimum
C. $(0, -6)$; minimum **D.** $(6, 0)$; minimum

3. ______

Assessment

4. What are the root(s) of the quadratic equation whose related function is graphed at the right?

A. 4, 0 **B.** −2, 3
C. 2, 3 **D.** −4, 0

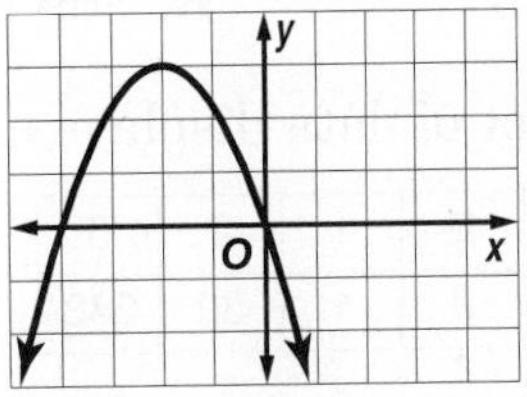

4. ______

5. One root of the quadratic equation whose related function is graphed lies between which consecutive integers?

A. −4 and −3 **B.** 0 and 1
C. −5 and −4 **D.** −3 and −2

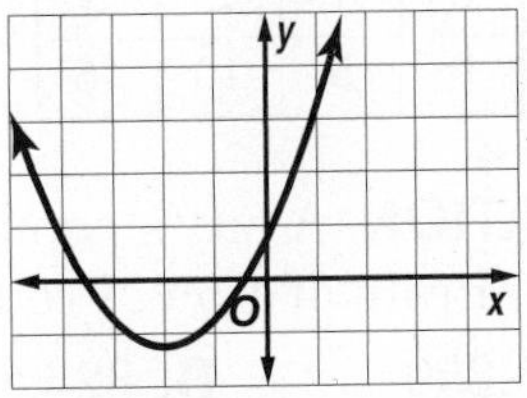

5. ______

6. Solve $b^2 - 16b + 64 = 9$ by taking the square root of each side.

A. −5, −11 **B.** 17 **C.** ±17 **D.** 5, 11

6. ______

7. Which step is *not* performed in the process of solving $r^2 + 12r - 6 = 0$ by completing the square?

A. Add 6 to each side. **B.** Factor $r^2 + 12r - 6$.
C. Add 36 to each side. **D.** Take the square root of each side.

7. ______

8. Which equation is equivalent to $3x^2 + 24x + 15 = 0$?

A. $(x + 4)^2 = 11$ **B.** $(x + 4)^2 = 1$ **C.** $(x + 2)^2 = -1$ **D.** $(x + 2)^2 = -11$

8. ______

For Questions 9 and 10, solve each equation by using the Quadratic Formula. Round to the nearest tenth if necessary.

9. $3x^2 - 11x - 4 = 0$

A. $-4, \frac{1}{3}$ **B.** 0.4, 3.3 **C.** $-\frac{1}{3}, 4$ **D.** −3.3, −0.4

9. ______

10 Chapter 10 Test, Form 2B *(continued)*

10. $d^2 + 4 = 6d$

A. −5.2, −0.8 **B.** −6.6, 0.6 **C.** −0.6, 6.6 **D.** 0.8, 5.2 **10.** _____

11. Determine the number of real roots of $6x^2 + 19x + 14$.

A. 2 **B.** infinitely many **C.** 1 **D.** none **11.** _____

12. State the value of the discriminant for $3b^2 + 6b = 10$.

A. −84 **B.** 156 **C.** 126 **D.** 12.5 **12.** _____

13. Which equation corresponds to the graph shown?

A. $y = 3^x + 2$ **B.** $y = 2(3^x + 1)$

C. $y = 2(3^x)$ **D.** $y = (2 \cdot 3)^x + 1$ **13.** _____

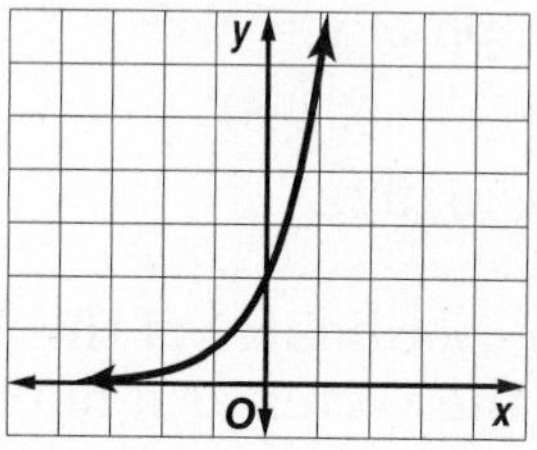

14. A weight lifter can deadlift 275 pounds. She can increase the weight $W(x)$ that she can lift according to the function $W(x) = 275(1.05)^x$, where x represents the number of training cycles completed. How much will she deadlift after 5 training cycles?

A. 334 lb **B.** 369 lb **C.** 344 lb **D.** 351 lb **14.** _____

15. Which set of data displays exponential behavior?

A.

x	0	1	2	3
y	0	1	32	243

B.

x	0	1	2	3
y	1	5	25	125

C.

x	0	1	2	3
y	0	5	10	15

D.

x	0	1	2	3
y	20	10	5	1

15. _____

16. POPULATION A city's population is about 763,000 and is increasing at an annual rate of 1.5%. Predict the population of the city in 50 years.

A. 1,335,250 **B.** 826,830,628 **C.** 358,374 **D.** 1,606,300 **16.** _____

17. BUSINESS A printing press valued at $120,000 depreciates 12% per year. What will be the approximate value of the printing press in 7 years?

A. $19,200 **B.** $265,282 **C.** $49,041 **D.** $55,728 **17.** _____

18. Determine which sequence is geometric.

A. −2, −10, −50, −250, ... **B.** 7, 10, 13, 16, ...

C. −16, 12, −8, 4, ... **D.** 21, 17, 13, 9, ... **18.** _____

19. Find the sixth term of a geometric sequence in which $a_1 = -7$ and $r = 3$.

A. −5103 **B.** −1701 **C.** −126 **D.** −448 **19.** _____

20. Find the geometric mean in the sequence −18, ____, −648.

A. 333 or −333 **B.** 168 or −168 **C.** 108 or −108 **D.** 228 or −228 **20.** _____

Bonus Find all values of c that make $x^2 + cx + 64$ a perfect square. **B:** _______________

NAME ______________________ DATE ____________ PERIOD ______

10 Chapter 10 Test, Form 2C

SCORE ______

For Questions 1 and 2, use a table of values to graph each function.

1. $y = -x^2 + 3x + 10$

1.

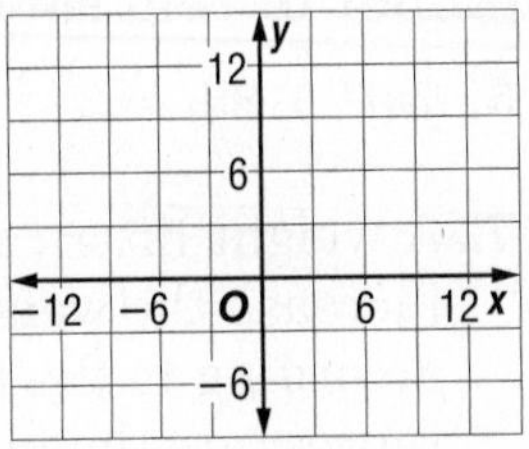

2. $y = 2x^2 - 3x$

2.

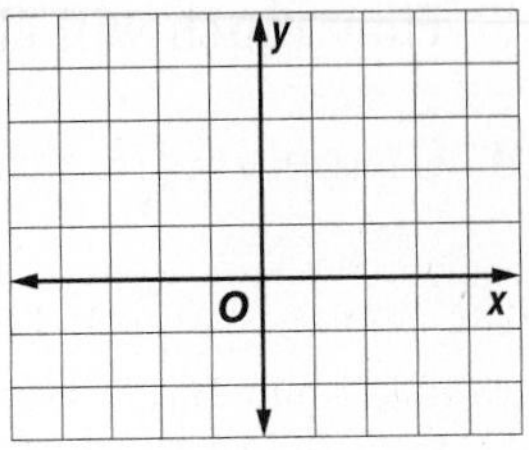

3. Write the equation of the axis of symmetry, and find the coordinates of the vertex of the graph of $y = 2x^2 - 8x + 3$. Identify the vertex as a maximum or a minimum.

3. ____________

Solve each equation by graphing. If integral roots cannot be found, estimate the roots by stating the consecutive integers between which the roots lie.

4. $x^2 - 6x + 9 = 0$

5. $x^2 - 6x + 4 = 0$

6. $2x^2 - 7x - 39 = 0$

4. ____________

5. ____________

6. ____________

Solve each equation by taking the square root of each side. Round to the nearest tenth if necessary.

7. $t^2 - 2t + 1 = 10$

8. $w^2 + 20w + 100 = 169$

7. ____________

8. ____________

Solve each equation by completing the square. Round to the nearest tenth if necessary.

9. $2x^2 + 3x = 20$

10. $p^2 - 12p + 9 = 0$

9. ____________

10. ____________

For Questions 11 and 12, solve each equation by using the Quadratic Formula. Round to the nearest tenth if necessary.

11. $15n^2 - 3 = 4n$

12. $r^2 + 16r + 21 = 0$

11. ____________

12. ____________

13. Determine whether the sequence 0.25, 1, 4, 16, 64, … is geometric.

13. ____________

14. Find the next three terms in the geometric sequence. 2, −16, 128, −1024, …

14. ____________

Assessment

NAME ______________________ DATE ____________ PERIOD ______

10 Chapter 10 Test, Form 2C *(continued)*

For Questions 15 and 16, state the value of the discriminant for each equation. Then determine the number of real roots of the equation.

15. $7m^2 + 8m = 3$ 16. $4p^2 = 4p - 1$

15. ____________

16. ____________

17. A weight lifter can bench-press 165 pounds. She plans to increase the weight $W(x)$ in pounds that she is lifting according to the function $W(x) = 165(1.05)^x$, where x represents the number of training cycles she completes. How much will she bench-press after 4 training cycles?

17. ____________

18. Graph $y = 7^x$. State the y-intercept.

18.

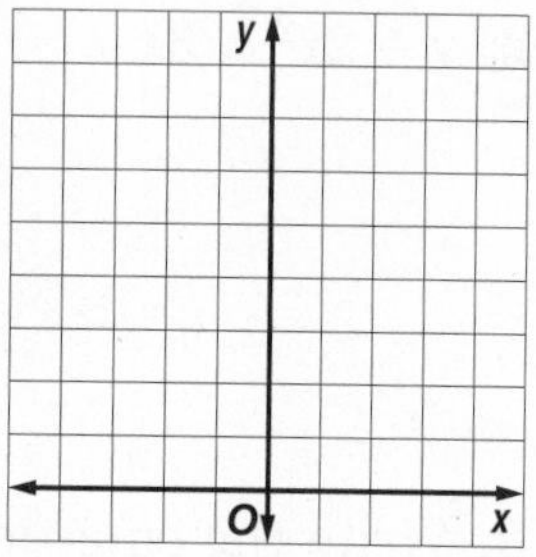

____

19. Use the graph of $y = 7^x$ to determine the approximate value of $7^{0.6}$.

19. ____________

For Questions 20 and 21, determine whether the data in each table display exponential behavior. Explain why or why not.

20.

x	1	2	3	4
y	−4	12	−48	192

20. ____________

21.

x	2	5	8	11	14
y	2	6	18	54	162

21. ____________

22. **INVESTMENTS** Determine the amount of an investment if \$700 is invested at an interest rate of 8% compounded monthly for 9 years.

22. ____________

23. **BUSINESS** A new welding machine valued at \$38,000 depreciates at a steady rate of 9% per year. What is the value of the welding machine in 10 years?

23. ____________

24. Find the fourth term of a geometric sequence in which $a_1 = -3$ and $r = 7$.

24. ____________

25. Find the geometric mean in the sequence 4, ____, 576.

25. ____________

Bonus Without graphing, determine the x-intercepts of the graph of $f(x) = 7x^2 + 9x + 1$.

B: ____________

NAME ____________________ DATE __________ PERIOD _____

10 Chapter 10 Test, Form 2D

SCORE _____

For Questions 1 and 2, use a table of values to graph each function.

1. $y = x^2 - 7x + 12$

1.

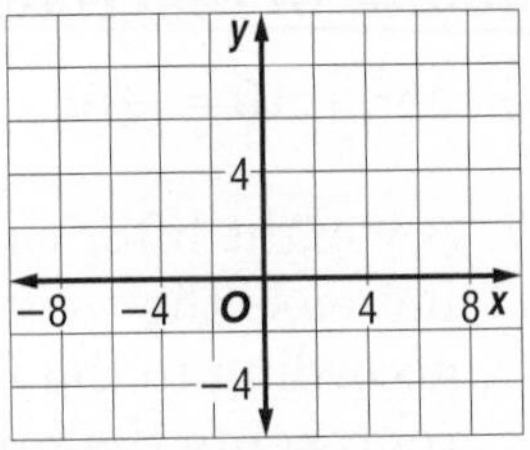

2. $y = 4x^2 - 8x$

2.

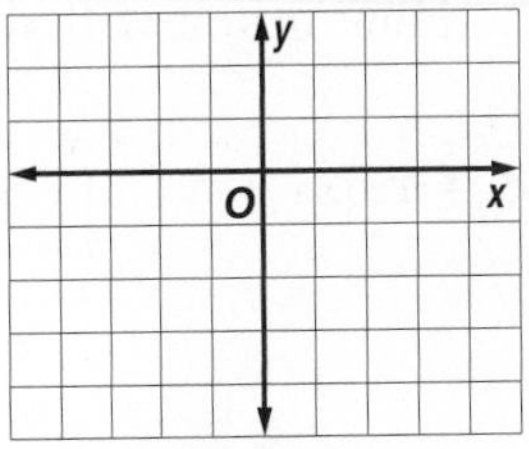

3. Write the equation of the axis of symmetry, and find the coordinates of the vertex of the graph of $y = -2x^2 + 4x - 5$. Identify the vertex as a maximum or a minimum.

3. __________

Solve each equation by graphing. If integral roots cannot be found, estimate the roots by stating the consecutive integers between which the roots lie.

4. $x^2 - 4x + 3 = 0$

4. __________

5. $x^2 - 2x - 1 = 0$

5. __________

6. $3x^2 - 8x - 35 = 0$

6. __________

Solve each equation by taking the square root of each side. Round to the nearest tenth if necessary.

7. $m^2 - 18m + 81 = 100$

8. $r^2 + 10r + 25 = 15$

7. __________

8. __________

Solve each equation by completing the square. Round to the nearest tenth if necessary.

9. $2x^2 + 9x = 18$

10. $t^2 + 15t + 11 = 0$

9. __________

10. __________

For Questions 11 and 12, solve each equation by using the Quadratic Formula. Round to the nearest tenth if necessary.

11. $12v^2 - 6 = -v$

12. $d^2 - 14d + 22 = 0$

11. __________

12. __________

13. Determine whether the sequence 1, 2, 4, 7, 11, … is geometric.

13. __________

14. Find the next three terms in the geometric sequence 3, −18, 108, −648, … .

14. __________

Assessment

NAME ______________________________ DATE ____________ PERIOD ______

10 Chapter 10 Test, Form 2D *(continued)*

For Questions 15 and 16, state the value of the discriminant for each equation. Then determine the number of real roots of the equation.

15. $3b^2 + 10 = -8b$ **16.** $9a^2 = 6a - 1$

15. ____________

16. ____________

17. A weight lifter can bench-press 145 pounds. She plans to increase the weight $W(x)$ in pounds that she is lifting according to the function $W(x) = 145(1.05)^x$, where x represents the number of training cycles she completes. How much will she bench-press after 5 training cycles?

17. ____________

18. Graph $y = \left(\frac{1}{6}\right)^x$. State the y-intercept.

18.

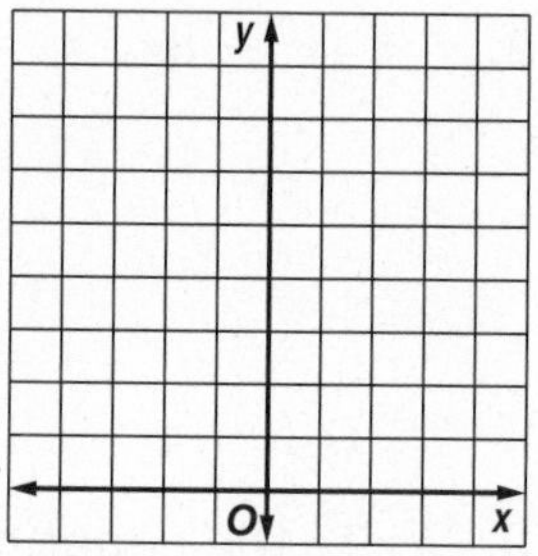

____

19. Use the graph of $y = \left(\frac{1}{6}\right)^x$ to determine the approximate value of $\left(\frac{1}{6}\right)^{-0.7}$.

19. ____________

For Questions 20 and 21, determine whether the data in each table display exponential behavior. Explain why or why not.

20.

x	1	2	3	4
y	2	5	8	11

20. ____________

21.

x	−1	1	3	5	7
y	7	14	28	56	112

21. ____________

22. ART An oil painting originally cost \$2500 and increases in value at a rate of 6% per year. Find the value of the painting after 12 years.

22. ____________

23. CARS A new car valued at \$16,500 depreciates at a steady rate of 12% per year. What is the value of the car in 10 years?

23. ____________

24. Find the fifth term of a geometric sequence in which $a_1 = 4$ and $r = -6$.

24. ____________

25. Find the geometric mean in the sequence 3, ____, 675.

25. ____________

Bonus Find the value of a so that the equation $ax^2 + 8x + 32 = 0$ has 1 real root.

B: ____________

NAME ______________________ DATE ____________ PERIOD _______

10 Chapter 10 Test, Form 3

SCORE _______

For Questions 1 and 2, use a table of values to graph each function.

1. $y = -2x^2 - 3x + 3$

1. 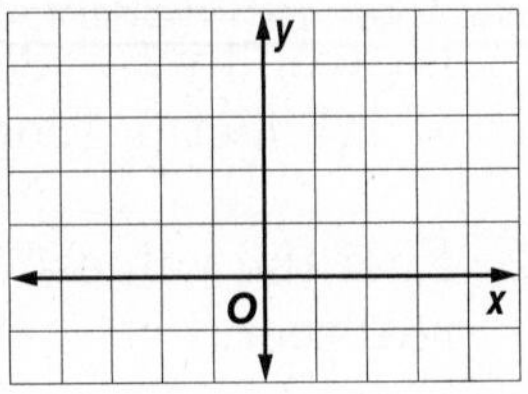

2. $y = 3x^2 - 5x - 2$

2. 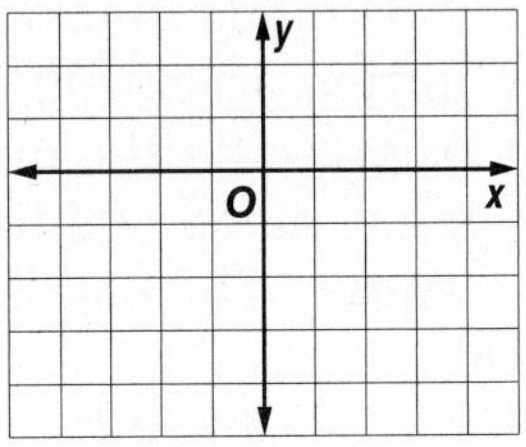

3. Write the equation of the axis of symmetry, and find the coordinates of the vertex of the graph of $y - 1 = 5x^2 - 25x + 3$. Identify the vertex as a maximum or a minimum.

3. ____________

Solve each equation by graphing. If integral roots cannot be found, estimate the roots by stating the consecutive integers between which the roots lie.

4. $\frac{1}{2}x^2 + x - 4 = 0$ 4. ____________

5. $x^2 + 7 = 6x$ 5. ____________

6. $6 = 3m^2 + 2m$ 6. ____________

For Questions 7 and 8, solve each equation by taking the square root of each side. Round to the nearest tenth if necessary.

7. $s^2 + 26s + 169 = 121$ 7. ____________

8. $b^2 - 34b + 289 = 45$ 8. ____________

9. Solve $3y^2 - 7y - 5 = 0$ by completing the square. Round to the nearest tenth if necessary. 9. ____________

10. Solve $x^2 + 10x + c = 0$ for x by completing the square. 10. ____________

11. Solve $21u^2 = u + 10$ by using the Quadratic Formula. Round to the nearest tenth if necessary. 11. ____________

Assessment

NAME ______________________ DATE ____________ PERIOD ________

10 Chapter 10 Test, Form 3 *(continued)*

12. PHYSICAL SCIENCE A projectile is shot vertically in the air from ground level. Its height h, in feet, after t seconds is given by $h = 88t - 16t^2$. Will the projectile have a height of 125 feet 0, 1, or 2 times after being shot?

12. ____________

13. Find the values for c so that $s^2 + cs + 81 = 0$ has one real root.

13. ____________

14. WEIGHT LIFTING A weight lifter can squat 475 pounds. She plans to increase the weight $W(x)$ in pounds that she is lifting according to the function $W(x) = 475(1.05)^x$, where x represents the number of training cycles she completes. How many training cycles must she complete to be able to squat 575 pounds?

14. ____________

15. Graph $y = 4(2^x - 1)$. State the y-intercept.

15.

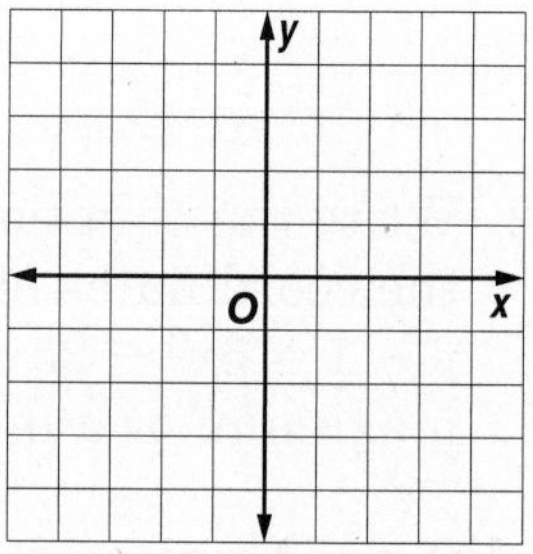

____

Determine whether the data in the table displays exponential behavior. Explain why or why not.

16.

x	0	1	2	3	4
y	10	20	40	80	160

16. ____________

17. INVESTMENTS Determine the amount of an investment if \$96,000 is invested at an interest rate of 5.2% compounded daily for 3 years.

17. ____________

18. Determine whether the sequence 25, −35, 49, −68.6, … is geometric.

18. ____________

19. Find the next three terms in the geometric sequence $\frac{7}{8}, \frac{7}{12}, \frac{7}{18}, \frac{7}{27}, \ldots$.

19. ____________

20. Find the missing terms in the geometric sequence 32, ____, 72, ____, 162.

20. ____________

Bonus Solve the equation $ax^2 + 7x - 4 = 0$ for x by using the Quadratic Formula.

B: ____________

NAME ______________________ DATE ____________ PERIOD ______

10 Chapter 10 Open-Ended Assessment

SCORE ______

Demonstrate your knowledge by giving a clear, concise solution to each problem. Be sure to include all relevant drawings and justify your answers. You may show your solution in more than one way or investigate beyond the requirements of the problem.

1. Write a quadratic function whose graph opens upward. Write an exponential function. Graph both functions on the same coordinate plane. Compare and contrast the domains and ranges of the two functions and any symmetry of the two graphs.

2. a. Write a quadratic equation that has no real roots, and find its discriminant. Explain how the discriminant shows that a quadratic equation has no real roots.

b. Write a quadratic equation that has one real root, and find its discriminant. Explain why the Quadratic Formula yields only one solution when the discriminant of a quadratic equation is equal to zero.

c. Write a quadratic equation that has two real roots. Determine whether completing the square, graphing, or factoring would be the better method to use to solve your quadratic equation.

3. Honovi purchased a new car for \$25,000 and has \$5000 left to invest.

a. Choose an interest rate between 4% and 7% for Honovi's investment, and find the length of time it would take for the investment to double.

b. Choose an annual depreciation rate from 8% to 10% for the new car that Honovi purchased, and find the length of time it would take for the car's value to be equal to one-half of the purchase price.

c. Using the rates from part **a** and part **b**, find the length of time it would take for the investment to be equal to the value of the car. What is the value at that time?

4. a. Write an exponential function, $f(x)$, and evaluate the function at $x = -1, 0, 1, 2, 3$, and 4. Do the function values form a geometric sequence? Explain your reasoning.

b. Give an example of a geometric sequence with a first term of 3. Compare and contrast your geometric sequence with the equation $y = 3 \cdot b^x$.

c. Describe how equations for exponential growth and exponential decay can be used to create geometric sequences.

Assessment

NAME ______________________ DATE ____________ PERIOD ________

10 Chapter 10 Vocabulary Test/Review

SCORE ________

axis of symmetry	exponential decay	maximum	quadratic function
common ratio	exponential function	minimum	roots
completing the square	exponential growth	parabola	symmetry
compound interest	geometric means	quadratic equation	vertex
discriminant	geometric sequence	Quadratic Formula	zeros

Write whether each sentence is *true* or *false*. If false, replace the underlined word or words to make a true sentence.

1. You need to find the values of x for which $f(x) = 0$ to find the <u>minimum</u> of a function. **1.** ____________

2. Symmetry is a geometric property of a <u>vertex</u>. **2.** ____________

3. You can use the discriminant to determine the number of <u>roots</u> of a quadratic equation. **3.** ____________

4. The formula for compound interest is a special case of the general equation for <u>exponential growth</u>. **4.** ____________

5. You can divide any term in a geometric sequence by the preceding term to find the <u>geometric means</u>. **5.** ____________

6. The <u>vertex</u> of a parabola is a minimum or maximum point. **6.** ____________

7. The equation $A = C(1 - r)^t$ is the general equation for <u>exponential decay</u>. **7.** ____________

8. The graph of a(n) <u>exponential function</u> is a parabola. **8.** ____________

9. Completing the square is a method you can use to solve a(n) <u>quadratic equation</u>. **9.** ____________

10. $y = 2^x$ is an example of a(n) <u>quadratic function</u>. **10.** ____________

In your own words—
Define each term.

11. axis of symmetry

12. geometric means

NAME ______________________ DATE ____________ PERIOD ________

10 Chapter 10 Quiz

(Lessons 10–1 and 10–2)

SCORE ________

1. Use a table of values to graph $y = 2x^2 - 8x + 4$.

1.
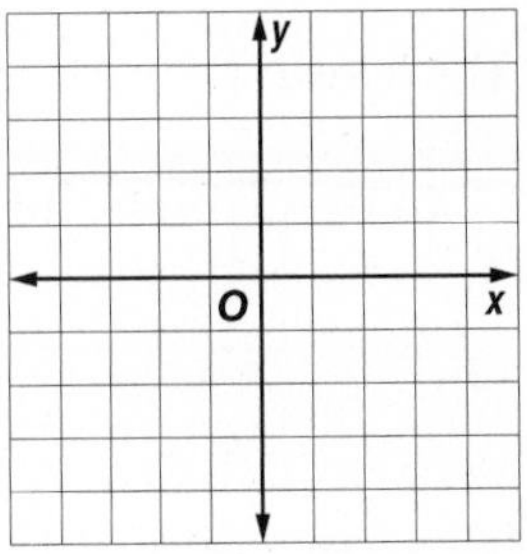

2. Write the equation of the axis of symmetry, and find the coordinates of the vertex of the graph of $y = -x^2 - 4x + 5$. Identify the vertex as a maximum or a minimum. Then graph the equation.

2.
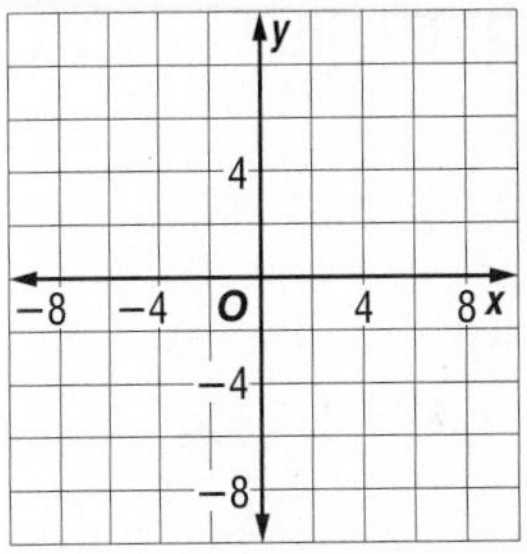

3. **Standardized Test Practice** Which graph corresponds with the equation $y + 2 = (x - 2)^2$?

A.
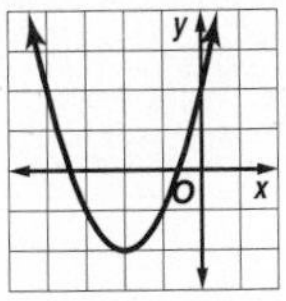

B.
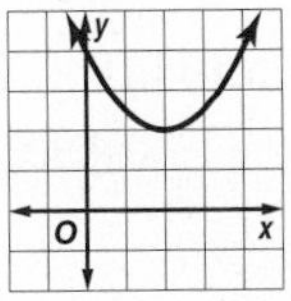

C.
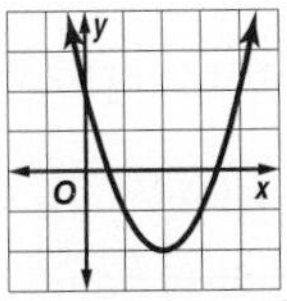

D.
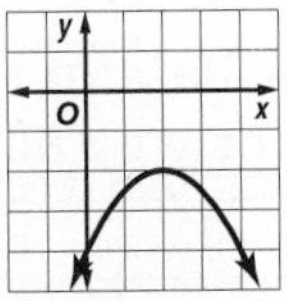

Solve each equation by graphing. If integral roots cannot be found, estimate the roots by stating the consecutive integers between which the roots lie.

4. $x^2 - 2x - 24 = 0$

5. $3m^2 - 6m + 1 = 0$

3. ____________

4. ____________

5. ____________

Assessment

NAME ______________________ DATE ____________ PERIOD ________

10 Chapter 10 Quiz

(Lessons 10–3 and 10–4)

SCORE ________

1. Solve $r^2 - 10r + 25 = 12$. Round to the nearest tenth if necessary. 1. ____________

2. Find the value of c that makes $p^2 + 9p + c$ a perfect square. 2. ____________

3. Solve $w^2 + 8w - 10 = 10$ by completing the square. Round to the nearest tenth if necessary. 3. ____________

4. Solve $4n^2 - 3n - 7 = 0$ by using the Quadratic Formula. Round to the nearest tenth if necessary. 4. ____________

5. State the value of the discriminant for $3y^2 = y - 14$. Then determine the number of real roots of the equation. 5. ____________

NAME ______________________ DATE __________ PERIOD ______

10 Chapter 10 Quiz

SCORE ______

(Lessons 10–5 and 10–6)

1. Graph $y = \left(\frac{1}{3}\right)^x$. State the y-intercept. Then use the graph to determine the approximate value of $\left(\frac{1}{3}\right)^{-1.7}$.

1.

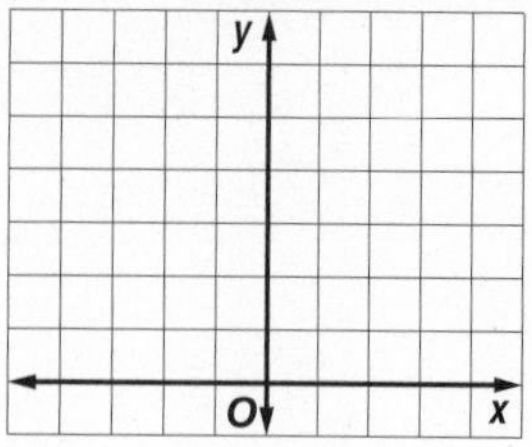

____

2. Graph $y = 4(2^x) - 1$. State the y-intercept.

2.

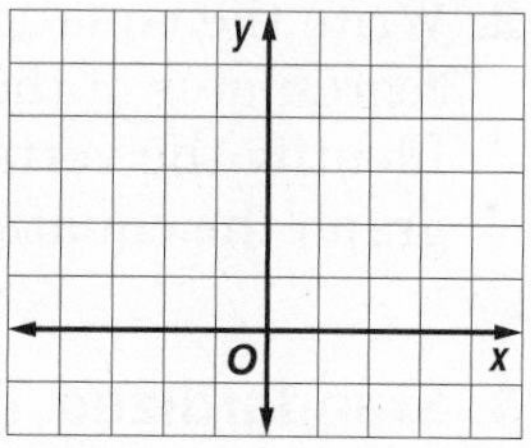

____

3. Determine whether the data in the table display exponential behavior. Explain why or why not.

x	−2	−1	0	1	2
y	−5	−3	−1	1	3

3. ______________

4. **INVESTMENTS** Determine the amount of an investment if \$1500 is invested at an interest rate of 4.85% compounded quarterly for 12 years.

4. ______________

5. **CARS** A new car costs \$35,000. It is expected to depreciate 8% each year. Find the value of the car in 7 years.

5. ______________

NAME ______________________ DATE __________ PERIOD ______

10 Chapter 10 Quiz

SCORE ______

(Lesson 10–7)

Determine whether each sequence is geometric.

1. −12, −5, 2, 9, …

1. ______________

2. 108, −36, 12, −4, …

2. ______________

3. Find the next three terms in the geometric sequence 6144, 1536, 384, 96, … .

3. ______________

4. Find the nth term of the geometric sequence with $a_1 = -5$, $n = 6$, and $r = 3$.

4. ______________

5. Find the geometric mean in the sequence −8, ____, −128.

5. ______________

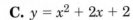

NAME _______________ DATE _______ PERIOD _______

10 Chapter 10 Mid-Chapter Test

SCORE _______

(Lessons 10–1 through 10–4)

Part I ***Write the letter for the correct answer in the blank at the right of each question.***

1. Which equation corresponds to the graph shown?

A. $y = x^2 - 2x + 2$ **B.** $y = -x^2 + 2x + 2$

C. $y = x^2 + 2x + 2$ **D.** $y = -x^2 - 2x + 2$ **1.** _______

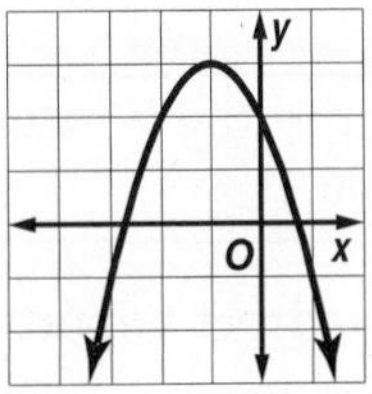

2. Find the coordinates of the vertex of the graph of $y = x^2 - 8x + 10$. Identify the vertex as a maximum or a minimum.

A. $(4, -6)$; minimum **B.** $(-4, 58)$; maximum

C. $(4, 6)$; maximum **D.** $(-4, 26)$; minimum **2.** _______

3. Solve $x^2 - 24x + 144 = 36$ by taking the square root of each side.

A. $-6, 18$ **B.** $6, 18$ **C.** $6, 12$ **D.** $-6, 6$ **3.** _______

4. Which equation is equivalent to $5b^2 + 30b - 10 = 0$?

A. $(b + 6)^2 = 38$ **B.** $(b + 6)^2 = 46$ **C.** $(b + 3)^2 = 11$ **D.** $(b + 3)^2 = 19$ **4.** _______

5. Which step is *not* performed in the process of solving $r^2 + 8r + 5 = 0$ by completing the square?

A. Subtract 5 from each side. **B.** Factor $r^2 + 8r$.

C. Add 16 to each side. **D.** Take the square root of each side. **5.** _______

6. State the value of the discriminant for $-2x^2 + 18 = 7x$.

A. 193 **B.** 13.9 **C.** -95 **D.** -130 **6.** _______

Assessment

Part II

Solve each equation by graphing. If integral roots cannot be found, estimate the roots by stating the consecutive integers between which the roots lie.

7. $x^2 - 4x + 5 = 0$ **7.** _______________

8. $x^2 - 7x - 8 = 0$ **8.** _______________

9. $2x^2 - 3x + 1 = 0$ **9.** _______________

10. $x^2 + 1 = 5x$ **10.** _______________

Solve each equation by using the Quadratic Formula. Round to the nearest tenth if necessary.

11. $-2x^2 + 18 = 7x$ **11.** _______________

12. $x^2 + 4x = -20$ **12.** _______________

NAME ______________________ DATE ____________ PERIOD ______

10

Chapter 10 Cumulative Review

(Chapters 1–10)

1. Solve the proportion $\frac{n}{500} = \frac{2}{40}$. (Lesson 3-6) — 1. ____________

2. Determine the x-intercept and y-intercept of $4x - 2y = 10$. (Lesson 4-5) — 2. ____________

3. Write a direct variation equation that relates x and y if $y = 10$ when $x = 12$. (Lesson 5-2) — 3. ____________

4. Solve $4y - 3(7y - 2) \leq -14 - 13y$. (Lesson 6-3) — 4. ____________

5. Solve the system of inequalities by graphing.
$x + y \leq 4$
$y \geq 2x - 4$ (Lesson 7-5) — 5.

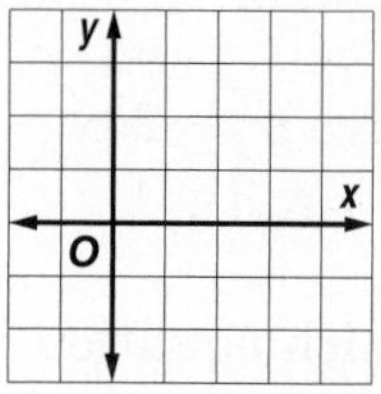

6. Arrange the terms of the polynomial $4x - 3 + 2x^2 + 3x^3$ so that the powers of x are in descending order. (Lesson 8-4) — 6. ____________

7. Simplify $(4xy + 3x^2y - 5y^2) - (3y^2 - 5xy + 7x^2y)$. (Lesson 8-5) — 7. ____________

8. Find $(3a^2 + 2)(3a^2 - 2)$. (Lesson 8-8) — 8. ____________

9. Factor $x^2 + 12x + 35$. (Lesson 9-3) — 9. ____________

10. Factor $2m^2 + 11m + 15$. (Lesson 9-4) — 10. ____________

11. Solve $36 - \frac{1}{4}y^2 = 0$ by factoring. (Lesson 9-5) — 11. ____________

12. Use a table of values to graph $y = -x^2 - 2x + 2$. (Lesson 10-1) — 12.

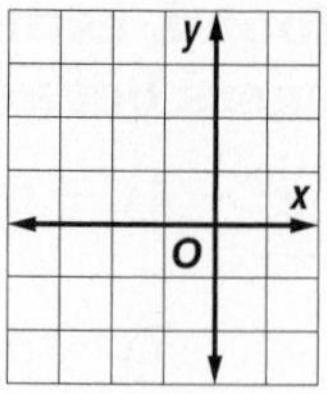

13. Use the formula $h = -16t^2 + 250t$ to model the height h in feet of a model rocket t seconds after it is launched. Determine when the rocket will reach a height of 900 feet. (Lesson 10-4) — 13. ____________

14. The population of North Carolina has been increasing at an annual rate of 1.7%. If the population of North Carolina was 7,650,789 in the year 1999, predict its population in 2010. (Lesson 10-6) — 14. ____________

NAME ____________________ DATE __________ PERIOD _____

10 Standardized Test Practice

(Chapters 1–10)

Part 1: Multiple Choice

Instructions: Fill in the appropriate oval for the best answer.

1. Armando collects baseball cards. He currently has 48 cards, and buys 5 new cards a week. How many cards will Armando have in 10 weeks? (Lesson 4-7)

A. 102 **B.** 98 **C.** 94 **D.** 100

1. Ⓐ Ⓑ Ⓒ Ⓓ

2. Wesley carves whistles out of wood and sells them at a gift shop. The equation $C = 2n + 15$ models his weekly cost C of making n whistles. The equation $R = 5n$ models his weekly revenue R from selling n whistles. How many whistles must Wesley make and sell for his cost and revenue to be equal? (Lesson 7-2)

E. 5 **F.** 4 **G.** 25 **H.** 10

2. Ⓔ Ⓕ Ⓖ Ⓗ

3. Evaluate $\frac{1.0701 \times 10^6}{4.35 \times 10^2}$. (Lesson 8-3)

A. 2.46×10^3
B. -3.2799×10^4
C. 5.4201×10^8
D. 0.246×10^4

3. Ⓐ Ⓑ Ⓒ Ⓓ

4. Find $3mn(2m^2 - 3mn + n^2)$. (Lesson 8-6)

E. $5m^3n - 6m^2n + 3mn^3$
F. $6m^2n - 3mn + 3mn^2$
G. $6m^3n - 9m^2n^2 + 3mn^3$
H. $2m^2 + n^2$

4. Ⓔ Ⓕ Ⓖ Ⓗ

5. Which binomial is a factor of $6ut - 9u + 8vt - 12v$? (Lesson 9-2)

A. $2t + 3$ **B.** $3u + 4$ **C.** $-2t + 3$ **D.** $3u + 4v$

5. Ⓐ Ⓑ Ⓒ Ⓓ

6. Factor $16 - n^4$. (Lesson 9-5)

E. $(4 - n^2)(4 + n^2)$
F. $(n + 2)(n - 2)(4 + n^2)$
G. $(2 - n)(2 + n)(n^2 + 4)$
H. $(2 - n)(2 + n)(2 - n)(2 + n)$

6. Ⓔ Ⓕ Ⓖ Ⓗ

7. Solve $2x^2 + 72 = 24x$. (Lesson 9-6)

A. $\{2, 6\}$ **B.** $\{-6, 2\}$ **C.** $\{6\}$ **D.** $\{-6\}$

7. Ⓐ Ⓑ Ⓒ Ⓓ

8. Find the coordinates of the vertex of the graph of $y = 3x^2 + 2x$. (Lesson 10-1)

E. $\left(\frac{1}{3}, 1\right)$ **F.** $\left(-\frac{1}{3}, -\frac{1}{3}\right)$ **G.** $\left(\frac{1}{3}, -\frac{1}{3}\right)$ **H.** $\left(-\frac{1}{3}, 1\right)$

8. Ⓔ Ⓕ Ⓖ Ⓗ

9. Which equation is equivalent to $2r^2 - 28r + 38 = 0$? (Lesson 10-3)

A. $2(r - 7)^2 = 49$
B. $(r - 14)^2 = 60$
C. $(r - 14)^2 = 177$
D. $(r - 7)^2 = 30$

9. Ⓐ Ⓑ Ⓒ Ⓓ

10. What number should be inserted into the table for the data to display exponential behavior? (Lesson 10-5)

x	2	3	4	5
y	8	24	72	

E. 152 **F.** 186 **G.** 248 **H.** 216

10. Ⓔ Ⓕ Ⓖ Ⓗ

Assessment

10 Standardized Test Practice *(continued)*

Part 2: Grid In

Instructions: Enter your answer by writing each digit of the answer in a column box and then shading in the appropriate oval that corresponds to that entry.

11. A watch is on sale for 30% off the original price. If the original price of the watch is \$14, what is the discounted price? (Lesson 3-7)

12. If $3x + 2y = 9$ and $3x + 3y = 6$, what is the value of x? (Lesson 7-3)

13. Evaluate $(7.1 \times 10^{12})(4.0 \times 10^{-10})$. Express the result in standard notation. (Lesson 8-3)

14. State the value of the discriminant for $4x^2 + 17x + 18 = 0$. (Lesson 10-4)

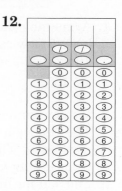

11.

12.

13.

14.

Part 3: Quantitative Comparison

Instructions: Compare the quantities in columns A and B. Shade in
- (A) if the quantity in column A is greater;
- (B) if the quantity in column B is greater;
- (C) if the quantities are equal; or
- (D) if the relationship cannot be determined from the information given.

	Column A	Column B	
15.	the arithmetic sequence $-14, -8, -2, 4, \ldots$		**15.** (A) (B) (C) (D)
	the common difference	the next term	
	(Lesson 4-7)		
16.	$2x + y = -1$ $5x - y = 22$		**16.** (A) (B) (C) (D)
	the value of x	the value of y	
	(Lesson 7-3)		
17.	the geometric sequence $3, -12, 48, -192, 768, \ldots$		**17.** (A) (B) (C) (D)
	the common ratio	the next term	
	(Lesson 10-7)		

NAME ______________________ DATE ____________ PERIOD ________

Unit 3 Test

(Chapters 8–10)

SCORE ________

1. Find the area of the triangle. 1. ____________

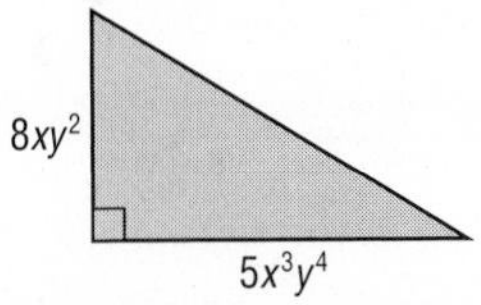

For Questions 2 and 3, simplify each expression. Assume that no denominator is equal to zero.

2. $(-2x^4)^3(-4x^2y^6)^3$ 2. ____________

3. $\frac{(3b^{-4}g^3)^{-2}}{(4b)^2}$ 3. ____________

4. Evaluate $\frac{4.03 \times 10^{-4}}{1.3 \times 10^2}$. Express your answer in scientific and standard notation. 4. ____________

5. Find the degree of the polynomial $4hk + 2h - k^3$. 5. ____________

6. Find $(4a - 2b + c) - (5c + a - 4b)$. 6. ____________

7. Solve $x(x - 3) = x(x + 5) - 16$. 7. ____________

For Questions 8–11, find each product.

8. $(p - 3)(p + 5)$ 8. ____________

9. $(a + 2)(a^2 - 3a - 7)$ 9. ____________

10. $(5t + s)^2$ 10. ____________

11. $(3k - 1)(3k + 1)$ 11. ____________

12. Find the GCF of $90m^2np^3$ and $150mn^3p^2$. 12. ____________

For Questions 13–16, factor each polynomial.

13. $4p^2q - 16pq + 8pq^2$ 13. ____________

14. $m^2 - 11m + 18$ 14. ____________

15. $3a^2 - 13a + 12$ 15. ____________

16. $27r^2 - 12s^2$ 16. ____________

17. The area of a square is $4p^2 - 4p + 1$ square inches. What is the length of the side of the square? 17. ____________

Assessment

Unit 3 Test *(continued)*

For Questions 18–22, solve each equation.

18. $22y^2 = -11y$ **18.** __________

19. $h^2 - 13h + 36 = 0$ **19.** __________

20. $5a^2 - 33a = 14$ **20.** __________

21. $24n^3 = 6n$ **21.** __________

22. $m^2 + 81 = -18m$ **22.** __________

23. Write the equation of the axis of symmetry, and find the coordinates of the vertex of the graph of $y = x^2 + 8x + 12$. Then graph $y = x^2 + 8x + 12$. **23.** __________

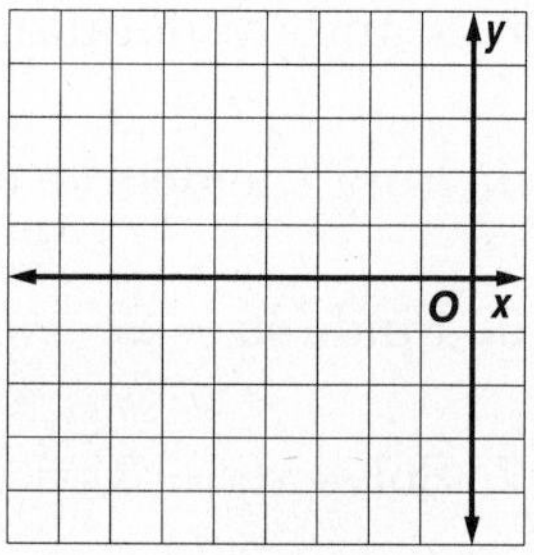

24. Solve $3x^2 + 2x + 1 = 0$ by graphing. **24.** __________

25. Solve $t^2 - 2t + 1 = 49$ by taking the square root of each side. **25.** __________

26. Solve $6 = 3t^2 + 2t$ by using the Quadratic Formula. Round to the nearest tenth if necessary. **26.** __________

27. Determine whether the data in the table display exponential behavior. Explain why or why not. **27.** __________

x	5	10	15	20
y	0	2	4	6

28. The population of Las Vegas, Nevada has been increasing at an annual rate of 7.0%. If the population of Las Vegas was 404,288 in the year 1999, predict its population in 2010. **28.** __________

29. A new motor home costs $89,000. It is expected to depreciate 9% each year. Find the value of the motor home in 4 years. **29.** __________

30. Find the next three terms in the geometric sequence 1458, 486, 162, 54, … . **30.** __________

NAME ______________________________ DATE ____________ PERIOD ______

10 Standardized Test Practice

Student Record Sheet *(Use with pages 580–581 of the Student Edition.)*

Part 1 *Multiple Choice*

Select the best answer from the choices given and fill in the corresponding oval.

1 Ⓐ Ⓑ Ⓒ Ⓓ	4 Ⓐ Ⓑ Ⓒ Ⓓ	7 Ⓐ Ⓑ Ⓒ Ⓓ
2 Ⓐ Ⓑ Ⓒ Ⓓ	5 Ⓐ Ⓑ Ⓒ Ⓓ	8 Ⓐ Ⓑ Ⓒ Ⓓ
3 Ⓐ Ⓑ Ⓒ Ⓓ	6 Ⓐ Ⓑ Ⓒ Ⓓ	9 Ⓐ Ⓑ Ⓒ Ⓓ

Part 2 *Short Response/Grid In*

Solve the problem and write your answer in the blank.

For Questions 14 and 15, also enter your answer by writing each number or symbol in a box. Then fill in the corresponding oval for that number or symbol.

10 ______________

11 ______________

12 ______________

13 ______________

14 ______________ (grid in)

15 ______________ (grid in)

14

	/	/	
.	.	.	.
	0	0	0
1	1	1	1
2	2	2	2
3	3	3	3
4	4	4	4
5	5	5	5
6	6	6	6
7	7	7	7
8	8	8	8
9	9	9	9

15

	/	/	
.	.	.	.
	0	0	0
1	1	1	1
2	2	2	2
3	3	3	3
4	4	4	4
5	5	5	5
6	6	6	6
7	7	7	7
8	8	8	8
9	9	9	9

Part 3 *Quantitative Comparison*

Select the best answer from the choices given and fill in the corresponding oval.

16 Ⓐ Ⓑ Ⓒ Ⓓ

17 Ⓐ Ⓑ Ⓒ Ⓓ

18 Ⓐ Ⓑ Ⓒ Ⓓ

19 Ⓐ Ⓑ Ⓒ Ⓓ

Part 4 *Open-Ended*

Record your answers for Question 20 on the back of this paper.

Answers

NAME ______________ DATE __________ PERIOD _____

10-1 Study Guide and Intervention

Graphing Quadratic Functions

Graph Quadratic Functions

Quadratic Function	a function described by an equation of the form $f(x) = ax^2 + bx + c$, where $a \neq 0$	**Example:** $y = 2x^2 + 3x + 8$

The degree of a quadratic function is 2, and the exponents are positive. Graphs of quadratic functions have a general shape called a **parabola**. A parabola opens upward and has a **minimum point** when the value of a is positive, and a parabola opens downward and has a **maximum point** when the value of a is negative.

Example 1 **Use a table of values to graph $y = x^2 - 4x + 1$.**

x	y
−1	6
0	1
1	−2
2	−3
3	−2
4	1

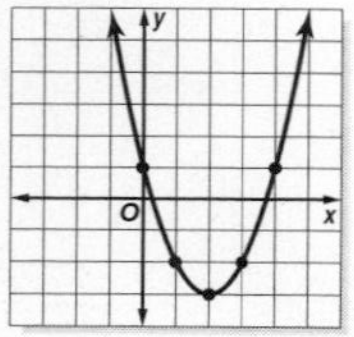

Graph the ordered pairs in the table and connect them with a smooth curve.

Example 2 **Use a table of values to graph $y = -x^2 - 6x - 7$.**

x	y
−6	−7
−5	−2
−4	1
−3	2
−2	1
−1	−2
0	−7

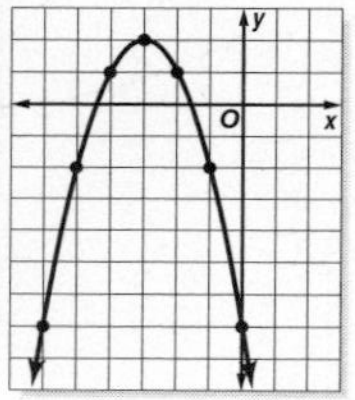

Graph the ordered pairs in the table and connect them with a smooth curve.

Lesson 10-1

Exercises

Use a table of values to graph each function.

1. $y = x^2 + 2$

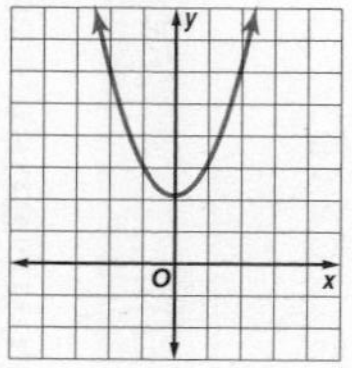

2. $y = -x^2 - 4$

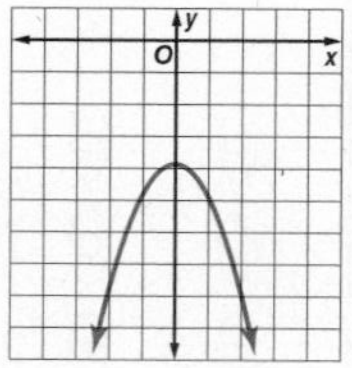

3. $y = x^2 - 3x + 2$

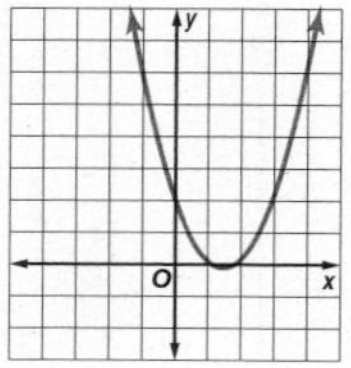

NAME ______________ DATE __________ PERIOD _____

10-1 Study Guide and Intervention *(continued)*

Graphing Quadratic Functions

Symmetry and Vertices Parabolas have a geometric property called **symmetry**. That is, if the figure is folded in half, each half will match the other half exactly. The vertical line containing the fold line is called the **axis of symmetry**.

Axis of Symmetry	For the parabola $y = ax^2 + bx + c$, where $a \neq 0$, the line $x = -\frac{b}{2a}$ is the axis of symmetry.	**Example:** The axis of symmetry of $y = x^2 + 2x + 5$ is the line $x = -1$.

The axis of symmetry contains the minimum or maximum point of the parabola, the **vertex**.

Example **Consider the graph of $y = 2x^2 + 4x + 1$.**

a. Write the equation of the axis of symmetry.

In $y = 2x^2 + 4x + 1$, $a = 2$ and $b = 4$. Substitute these values into the equation of the axis of symmetry.

$$x = -\frac{b}{2a}$$

$$x = -\frac{4}{2(2)} = -1$$

The axis of symmetry is $x = -1$.

b. Find the coordinates of the vertex.

Since the equation of the axis of symmetry is $x = -1$ and the vertex lies on the axis, the x-coordinate of the vertex is −1.

$y = 2x^2 + 4x + 1$ — Original equation

$y = 2(-1)^2 + 4(-1) + 1$ — Substitute.

$y = 2(1) - 4 + 1$ — Simplify.

$y = -1$

The vertex is at (−1, −1).

c. Identify the vertex as a maximum or a minimum.

Since the coefficient of the x^2-term is positive, the parabola opens upward, and the vertex is a minimum point.

d. Graph the function.

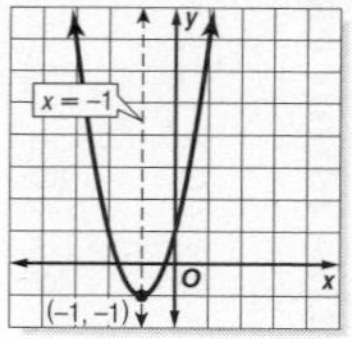

Exercises

Write the equation of the axis of symmetry, and find the coordinates of the vertex of the graph of each function. Identify the vertex as a maximum or a minimum. Then graph the function.

1. $y = x^2 + 3$
x = 0; (0, 3); min

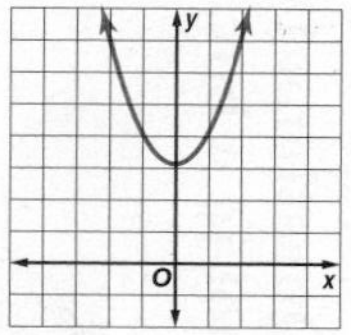

2. $y = -x^2 - 4x - 4$
x = −2; (−2, 0); max

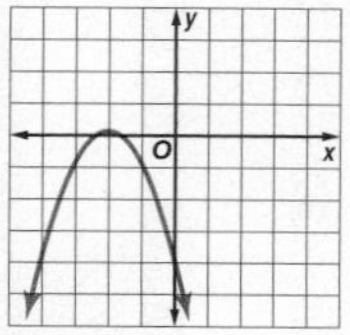

3. $y = x^2 + 2x + 3$
x = −1; (−1, 2); min

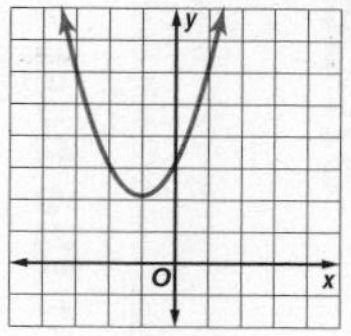

NAME ______________________ DATE __________ PERIOD _____

10-1 Skills Practice

Graphing Quadratic Functions

Use a table of values to graph each function.

1. $y = x^2 - 4$

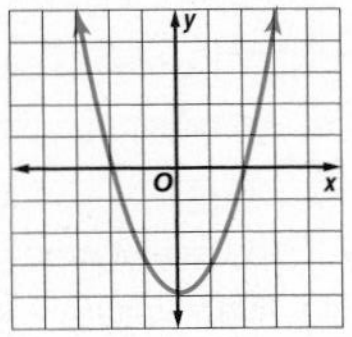

2. $y = -x^2 + 3$

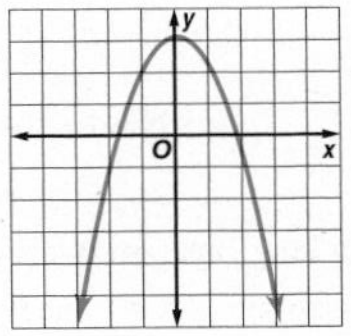

3. $y = x^2 - 2x - 6$

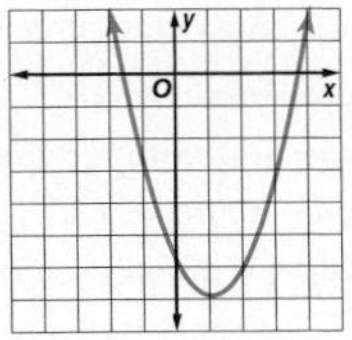

4. $y = -x^2 - 4x + 1$

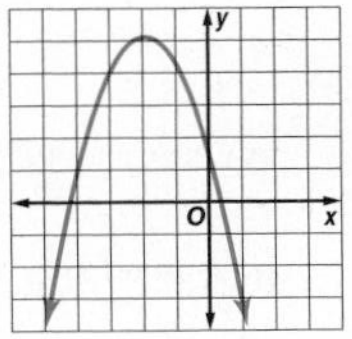

Write the equation of the axis of symmetry, and find the coordinates of the vertex of the graph of each function. Identify the vertex as a maximum or minimum. Then graph the function.

5. $y = 2x^2$
$x = 0$; (0, 0); min

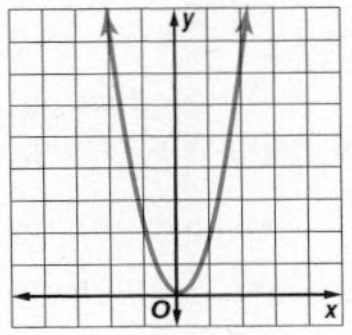

6. $y = x^2 - 2x - 5$
$x = 1$; (1, −6); min

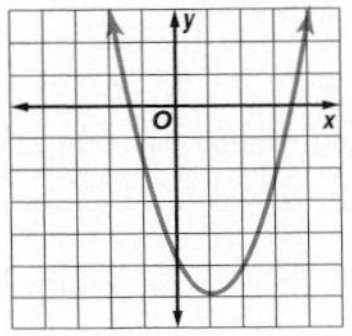

7. $y = -x^2 + 4x - 1$
$x = 2$; (2, 3); max

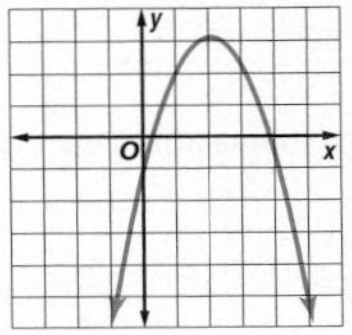

8. $y = -x^2 - 2x + 2$
$x = -1$; (−1, 3); max

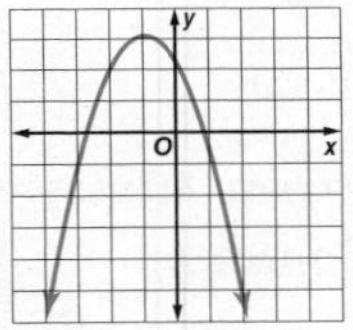

9. $y = 2x^2 + 4x - 2$
$x = -1$; (−1, −4); min

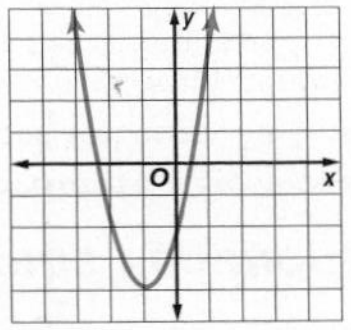

10. $y = -2x^2 - 4x + 6$
$x = -1$; (−1, 8); max

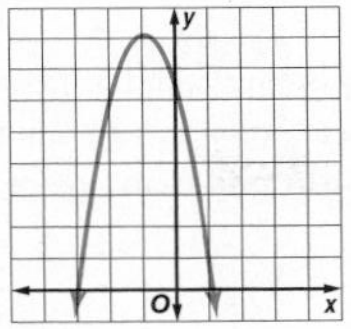

Lesson 10-1

NAME ______________________ DATE __________ PERIOD _____

10-1 Practice (Average)

Graphing Quadratic Functions

Use a table of values to graph each function.

1. $y = -x^2 + 2$

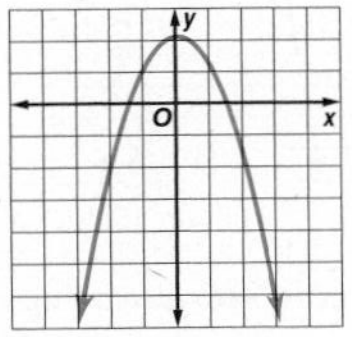

2. $y = x^2 - 6x + 3$

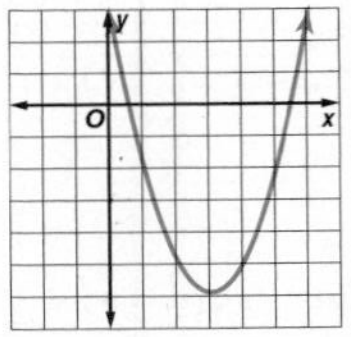

3. $y = -2x^2 - 8x - 5$

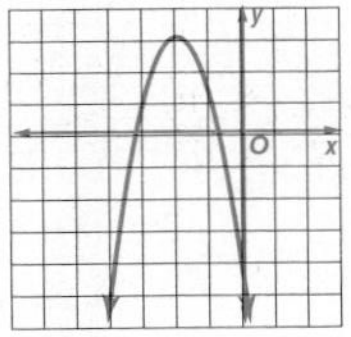

Write the equation of the axis of symmetry, and find the coordinates of the vertex of the graph of each function. Identify the vertex as a maximum or minimum. Then graph the function.

4. $y = -x^2 + 3$
$x = 0$; (0, 3); max

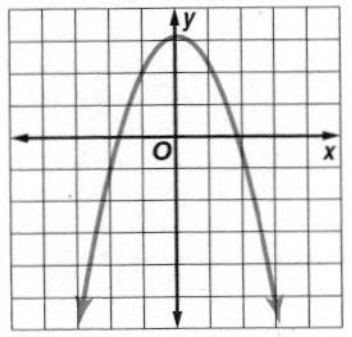

5. $y = -2x^2 + 8x - 3$
$x = 2$; (2, 5); max

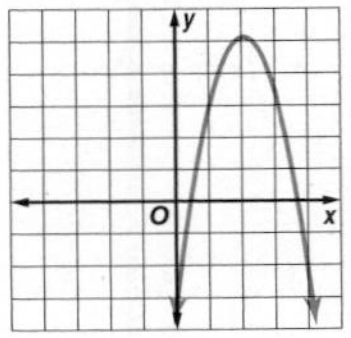

6. $y = 2x^2 + 8x + 1$
$x = -2$; (−2, −7); min

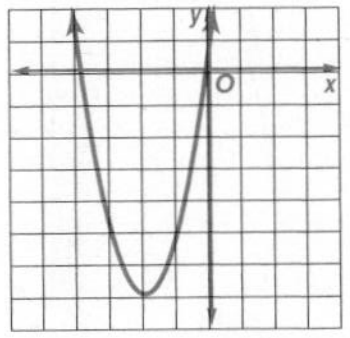

PHYSICS For Exercises 7–9, use the following information.

Miranda throws a set of keys up to her brother, who is standing on a third-story balcony with his hands 38 feet above the ground. If Miranda throws the keys with an initial velocity of 40 feet per second, the equation $h = -16t^2 + 40t + 5$ gives the height h of the keys after t seconds.

7. How long does it take the keys to reach their highest point? 1.25 s

8. How high do the keys reach? 30 ft

9. Will her brother be able to catch the keys? Explain. No, the keys will be 8 ft short of their target.

BASEBALL For Exercises 10–12, use the following information.

A player hits a baseball at a 45° angle with the ground with an initial velocity of 80 feet per second from a height of three feet above the ground. The equation $h = -0.005x^2 + x + 3$ gives the path of the ball, where h is the height and x is the horizontal distance the ball travels.

10. What is the equation of the axis of symmetry? $x = 100$

11. What is the maximum height reached by the baseball? 53 ft

12. An outfielder catches the ball three feet above the ground. How far has the ball traveled horizontally when the outfielder catches it? 200 ft

Answers

NAME ____________ DATE ________ PERIOD ____

10-1 Reading to Learn Mathematics

Graphing Quadratic Functions

Pre-Activity **How can you coordinate a fireworks display with recorded music?**

Read the introduction to Lesson 10-1 at the top of page 524 in your textbook.

According to the graph, at what height does the rocket explode and in how many seconds after being launched? **It explodes at a height of 80 meters 4 seconds after being launched.**

Reading the Lesson

1. The standard form for a **quadratic** function is $y = ax^2 + bx + c$. For the function $y = 2x^2 - 5x + 3$, the value of a is **2**, the value of b is **−5**, and the value of c is **3**.

2. The graphs of two quadratic functions are shown below. Complete each statement about the graphs.

A.

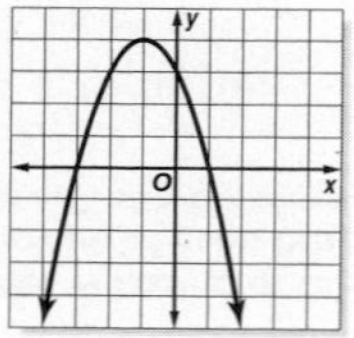

B.

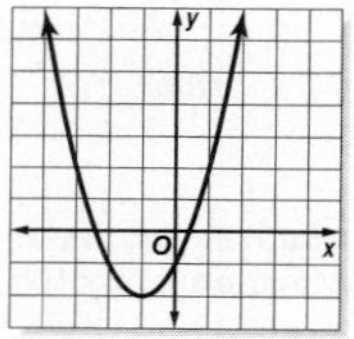

a. Each graph is a curve called a **parabola**.

b. The highest point of graph A is located at **(−1, 4)**. This point is the **maximum** (maximum/minimum) point of the graph.

c. The lowest point of graph B is located at **(−1, −2)**. This point is the **minimum** (maximum/minimum) point of the graph.

3. The maximum or minimum point of a parabola is called the **vertex** of the parabola.

4. If you fold a parabola along a line to get two halves that match exactly, the line where you fold the parabola is the **axis of symmetry** of the parabola. This line goes through the **vertex** of the parabola.

5. For a quadratic function $y = ax^2 + bx + c$, the parabola opens upward if a **>** 0. It opens downward if a **<** 0.

Helping You Remember

6. Look up the word *vertex* in a dictionary. You will find that it comes from the Latin word *vertere*, which means to turn. How can you use the idea of "to turn" to remember what the vertex of a parabola is? **Sample answer: The vertex of a parabola is the point at which the parabola turns upward or downward.**

Lesson 10-1

NAME ____________ DATE ________ PERIOD ____

10-1 Enrichment

Translating Quadratic Graphs

When a figure is moved to a new position without undergoing any rotation, then the figure is said to have been **translated** to that position.

The graph of a quadratic equation in the form $y = (x - b)^2 + c$ is a translation of the graph of $y = x^2$.

Start with $y = x^2$.

Slide to the right 4 units.

$y = (x - 4)^2$

Then slide up 3 units.

$y = (x - 4)^2 + 3$

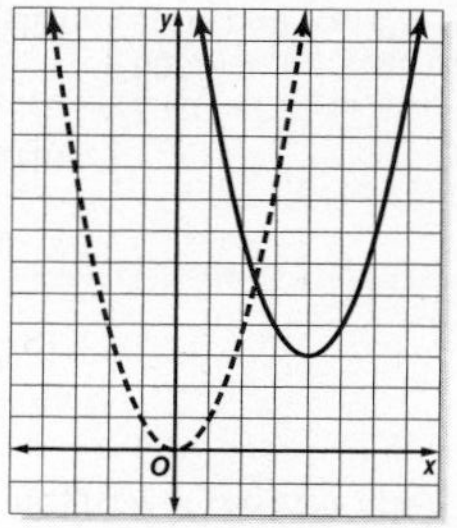

These equations have the form $y = x^2 + c$. Graph each equation.

1. $y = x^2 + 1$

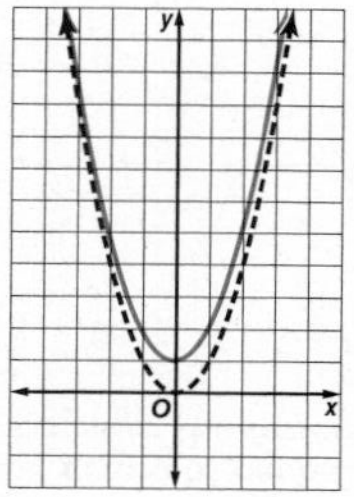

2. $y = x^2 + 2$

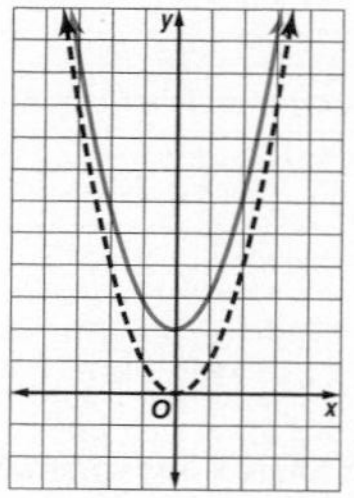

3. $y = x^2 - 2$

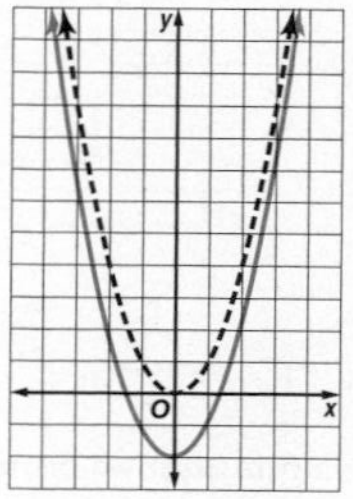

These equations have the form $y = (x - b)^2$. Graph each equation.

4. $y = (x - 1)^2$

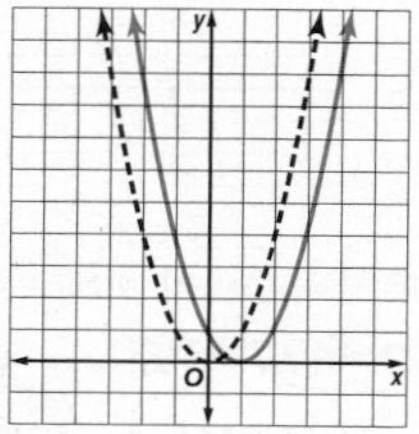

5. $y = (x - 3)^2$

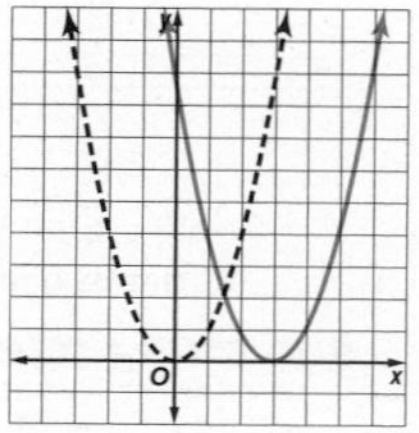

6. $y = (x + 2)^2$

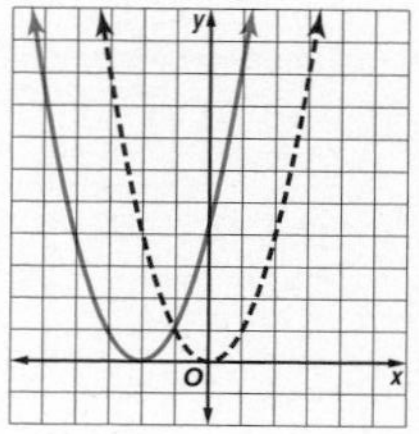

NAME ______________________ DATE ____________ PERIOD _____

10-2 Study Guide and Intervention

Solving Quadratic Equations by Graphing

Solve by Graphing

Quadratic Equation	an equation of the form $ax^2 + bx + c = 0$, where $a \neq 0$

The solutions of a quadratic equation are called the **roots** of the equation. The roots of a quadratic equation can be found by graphing the related quadratic function $f(x) = ax^2 + bx + c$ and finding the x-intercepts or **zeros** of the function.

Example 1 **Solve $x^2 + 4x + 3 = 0$ by graphing.**

Graph the related function $f(x) = x^2 + 4x + 3$. The equation of the axis of symmetry is $x = -\frac{4}{2(1)}$ or -2. The vertex is at $(-2, -1)$. Graph the vertex and several other points on either side of the axis of symmetry.

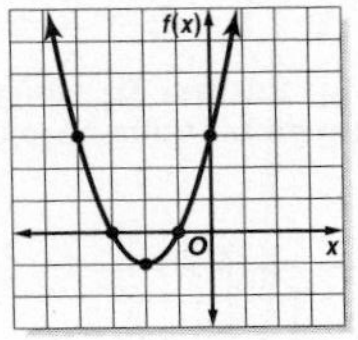

To solve $x^2 + 4x + 3 = 0$, you need to know where the value of $f(x) = 0$. This occurs at the x-intercepts, -3 and -1.
The solutions are -3 and -1.

Example 2 **Solve $x^2 - 6x + 9 = 0$ by graphing.**

Graph the related function $f(x) = x^2 - 6x + 9$. The equation of the axis of symmetry is $x = \frac{6}{2(1)}$ or 3. The vertex is at $(3, 0)$. Graph the vertex and several other points on either side of the axis of symmetry.

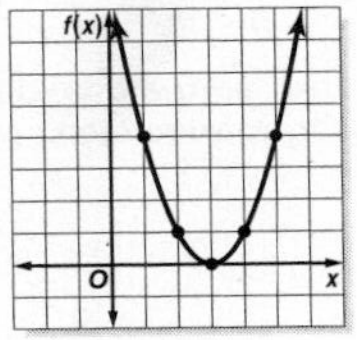

To solve $x^2 - 6x + 9 = 0$, you need to know where the value of $f(x) = 0$. The vertex of the parabola is the x-intercept. Thus, the only solution is 3.

Exercises

Solve each equation by graphing.

1. $x^2 + 7x + 12 = 0$

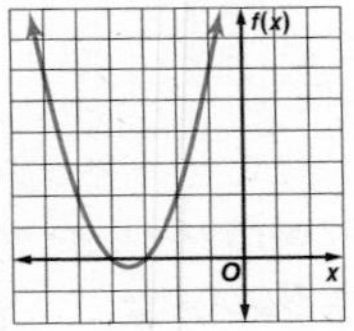

$-3; -4$

2. $x^2 - x - 12 = 0$

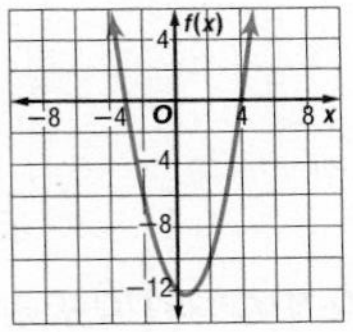

$4, -3$

3. $x^2 - 4x + 5 = 0$

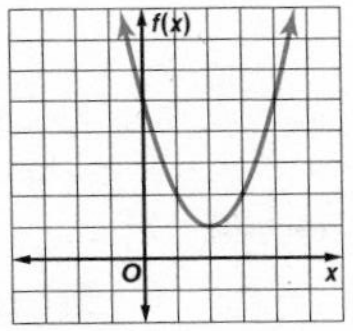

no real roots

Lesson 10-2

NAME ______________________ DATE ____________ PERIOD _____

10-2 Study Guide and Intervention *(continued)*

Solving Quadratic Equations by Graphing

Estimate Solutions The roots of a quadratic equation may not be integers. If exact roots cannot be found, they can be estimated by finding the consecutive integers between which the roots lie.

Example **Solve $x^2 + 6x + 6 = 0$ by graphing. If integral roots cannot be found, estimate the roots by stating the consecutive integers between which the roots lie.**

Graph the related function $f(x) = x^2 + 6x + 6$.

x	f(x)
−5	1
−4	−2
−3	−3
−2	−2
−1	1

Notice that the value of the function changes from negative to positive between the x-values of -5 and -4 and between -2 and -1.

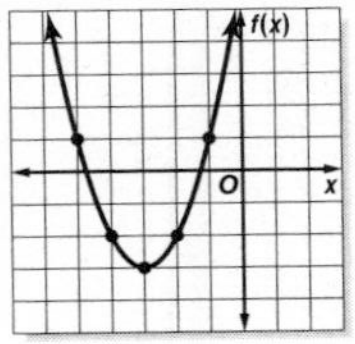

The x-intercepts of the graph are between -5 and -4 and between -2 and -1. So one root is between -5 and -4, and the other root is between -2 and -1.

Exercises

Solve each equation by graphing. If integral roots cannot be found, estimate the roots by stating the consecutive integers between which the roots lie.

1. $x^2 + 7x + 9 = 0$

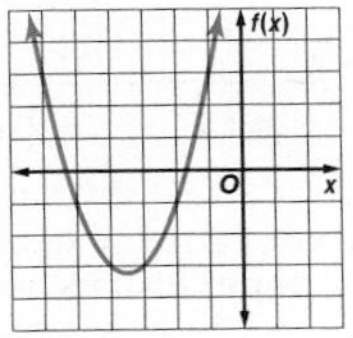

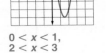

$-6 < x < -5$,
$-2 < x < -1$

2. $x^2 - x - 4 = 0$

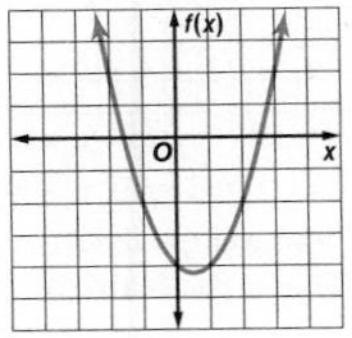

$-2 < x < -1$,
$2 < x < 3$

3. $x^2 - 4x + 6 = 0$

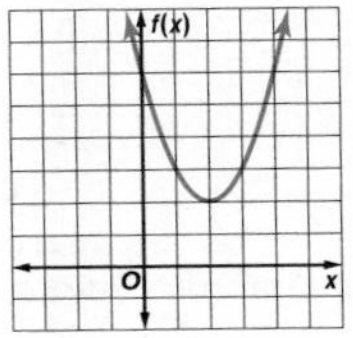

no real roots

4. $x^2 - 4x - 1 = 0$

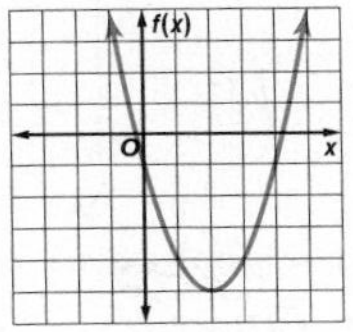

$-1 < x < 0$,
$4 < x < 5$

5. $4x^2 - 12x + 3 = 0$

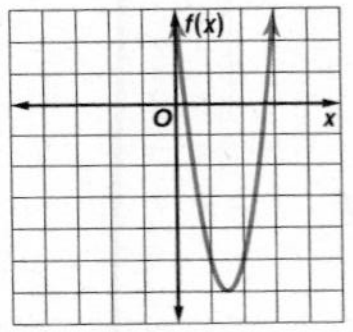

$0 < x < 1$,
$2 < x < 3$

6. $x^2 - 2x - 4 = 0$

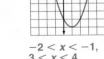

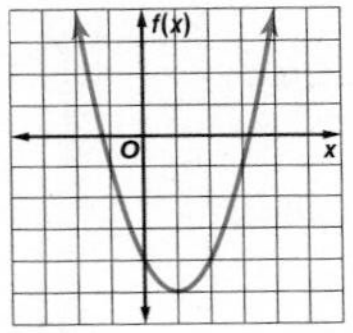

$-2 < x < -1$,
$3 < x < 4$

Answers

NAME ________________ DATE ________ PERIOD ____

10-2 Skills Practice

Solving Quadratic Equations by Graphing

Solve each equation by graphing.

1. $x^2 - 4x + 5 = 0$ **∅**

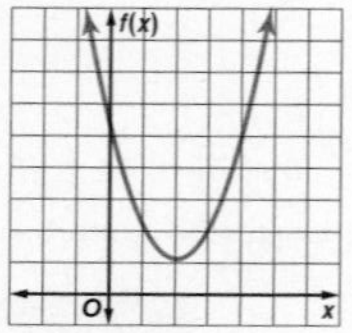

2. $c^2 + 6c + 8 = 0$ **−4, −2**

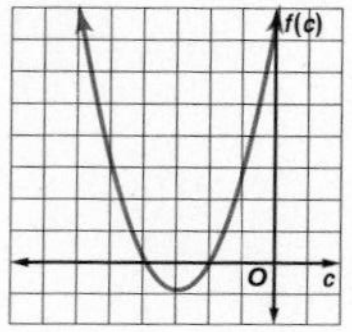

3. $a^2 - 2a = -1$ **1**

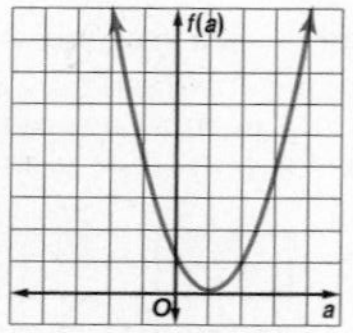

4. $n^2 - 7n = -10$ **2, 5**

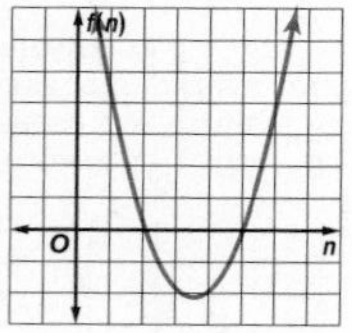

Solve each equation by graphing. If integral roots cannot be found, estimate the roots by stating the consecutive integers between which the roots lie.

5. $p^2 + 4p + 2 = 0$

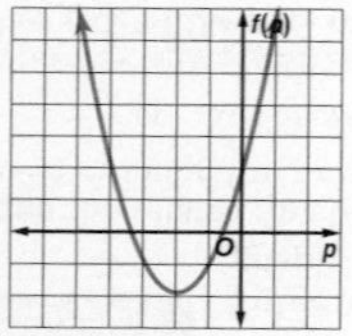

$-4 < p < -3, -1 < p < 0$

6. $x^2 + x - 3 = 0$

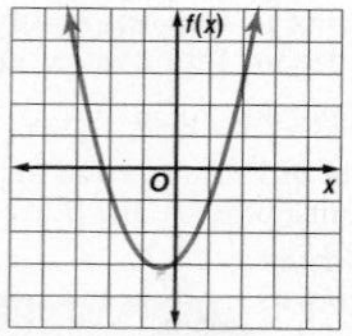

$-3 < x < -2, 1 < x < 2$

7. $d^2 + 6d = -3$

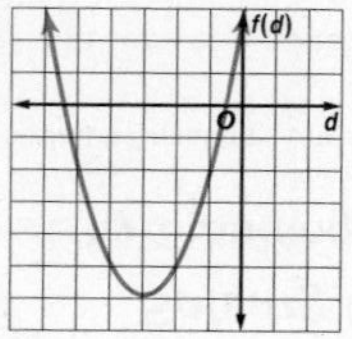

$-6 < d < -5, -1 < d < 0$

8. $h^2 + 1 = 4h$

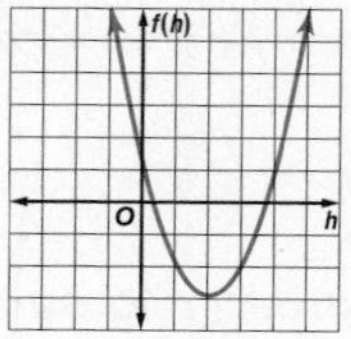

$0 < h < 1, 3 < h < 4$

Lesson 10-2

NAME ________________ DATE ________ PERIOD ____

10-2 Practice (Average)

Solving Quadratic Equations by Graphing

Solve each equation by graphing.

1. $x^2 - 5x + 6 = 0$ **2, 3**

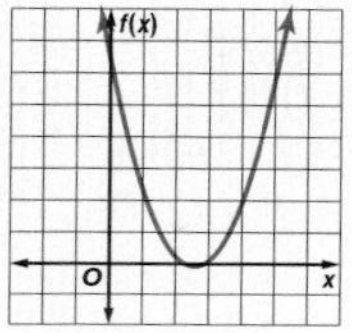

2. $w^2 + 6w + 9 = 0$ **−3**

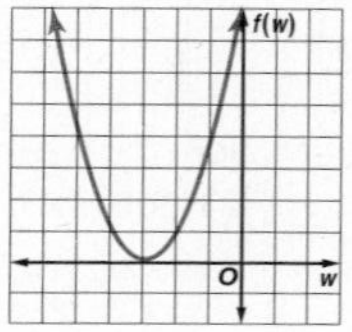

3. $b^2 - 4b + 5 = 0$ **∅**

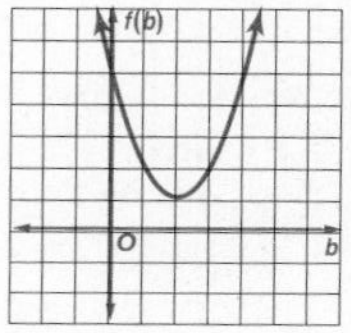

Solve each equation by graphing. If integral roots cannot be found, estimate the roots by stating the consecutive integers between which the roots lie.

4. $p^2 + 4p = 3$

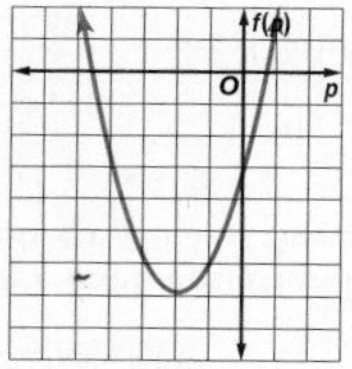

$-5 < p < -4$, $0 < p < 1$

5. $2m^2 + 5 = 10m$

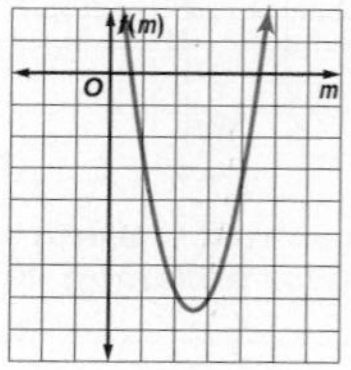

$0 < m < 1$, $4 < m < 5$

6. $2v^2 + 8v = -7$

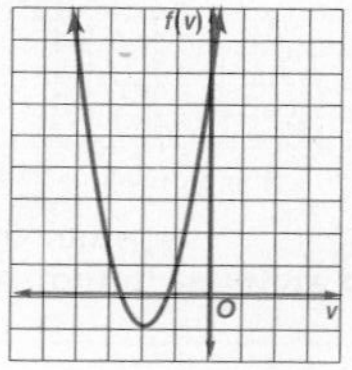

$-3 < v < -2$, $-2 < v < -1$

NUMBER THEORY For Exercises 7 and 8, use the following information.

Two numbers have a sum of 2 and a product of −8. The quadratic equation $-n^2 + 2n + 8 = 0$ can be used to determine the two numbers.

7. Graph the related function $f(n) = -n^2 + 2n + 8$ and determine its x-intercepts. **−2, 4**

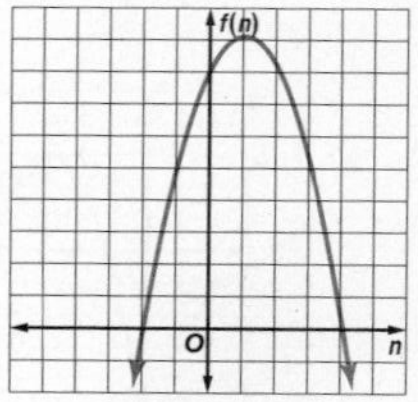

8. What are the two numbers? **−2 and 4**

DESIGN For Exercises 9 and 10, use the following information.

A footbridge is suspended from a parabolic support. The function $h(x) = -\frac{1}{25}x^2 + 9$ represents the height in feet of the support above the walkway, where $x = 0$ represents the midpoint of the bridge.

9. Graph the function and determine its x-intercepts. **−15, 15**

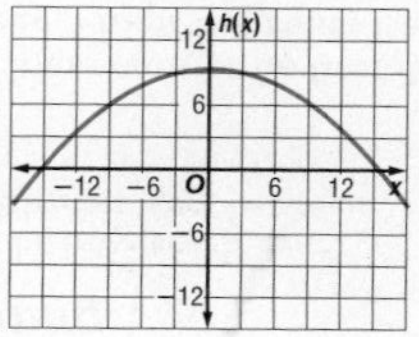

10. What is the length of the walkway between the two supports? **30 ft**

NAME ______________ DATE ________ PERIOD _____

10-2 Reading to Learn Mathematics

Solving Quadratic Equations by Graphing

Pre-Activity **How can quadratic equations be used in computer simulations?**

Read the introduction to Lesson 10-2 at the top of page 533 in your textbook.

If one of the x-intercepts represents the location where the ball will hit the ground, what does the other x-intercept represent? **The location where the ball is hit.**

Reading the Lesson

1. The x-intercepts of the graph of a quadratic function are the x-coordinates of the points where the graph of the function intersects the x-axis. At those points, the y-coordinates are equal to **0**. This explains why the x-intercepts are called **zeros** of the quadratic function.

2. The graphs of three functions are shown below. Use the graphs to provide the requested information about the related quadratic equations.

A. $f(x) = x^2 - 6x + 9$

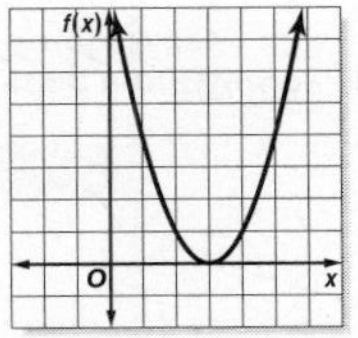

B. $f(x) = x^2 + 2x + 3$

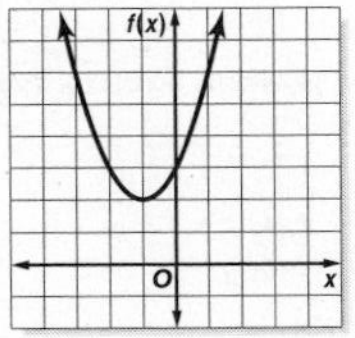

C. $f(x) = x^2 + x - 2$

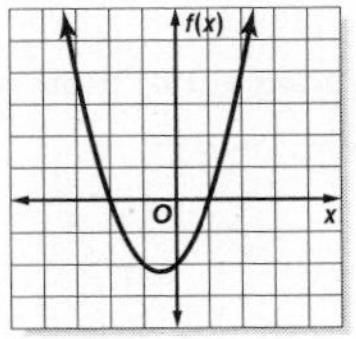

a. For Graph A, the related quadratic equation is **$x^2 - 6x + 9 = 0$**.

How many solutions are there? **one**

Name any solutions. **3**

b. For Graph B, the related quadratic equation is **$x^2 + 2x + 3 = 0$**.

How many solutions are there? **none**

Name any solutions. **none**

c. For Graph C, the related quadratic equation is **$x^2 + x - 2 = 0$**.

How many solutions are there? **two**

Name any solutions. **−2 and 1**

Helping You Remember

3. Describe how you can remember that the word *zero* is used when you are talking about functions, but the word *root* is used when you are talking about equations. **Sample answer: Some functions can have a value of zero. Equations can be true or false, but they do not have a number value.**

Lesson 10-2

NAME ______________ DATE ________ PERIOD _____

10-2 Enrichment

Odd Numbers and Parabolas

The solid parabola and the dashed stair-step graph are related. The parabola intersects the stair steps at their inside corners.

Use the figure for Exercises 1–3.

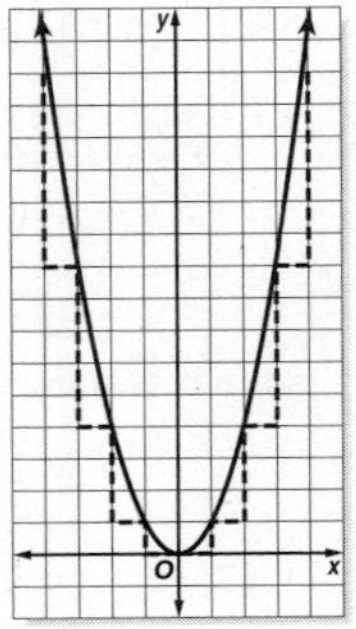

1. What is the equation of the parabola?

$y = x^2$

2. Describe the horizontal sections of the stair-step graph.

Each is 1 unit wide.

3. Describe the vertical sections of the stair-step graph.

They form the sequence 1, 3, 5, 7.

Use the second figure for Exercises 4–6.

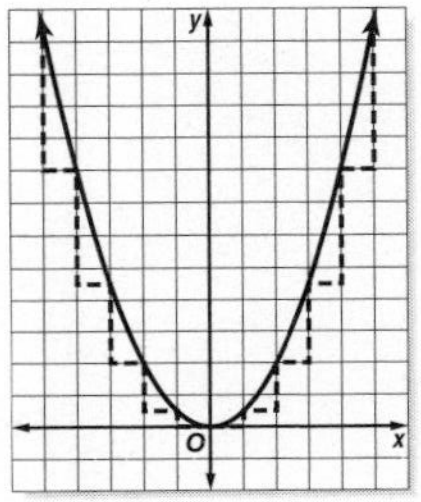

4. What is the equation of the parabola?

$y = \frac{1}{2}x^2$

5. Describe the horizontal sections of the stair steps.

Each is 1 unit wide.

6. Describe the vertical sections.

They form the sequence $\frac{1}{2}, \frac{3}{2}, \frac{5}{2}, \frac{7}{2}, \frac{9}{2}$.

7. How does the graph of $y = \frac{1}{2}x^2$ relate to the sequence of numbers $\frac{1}{2}, \frac{3}{2}, \frac{5}{2}, \frac{7}{2}, \ldots$?

If the x values increase by 1, the y values increase by the numbers in the sequence.

8. Complete this conclusion. To graph a parabola with the equation $y = ax^2$, start at the vertex. Then go over 1 and up a; over 1 and up $3a$;

over 1 and up $5a$; over 1 and up $7a$; and so on. The coefficients of a are the odd numbers.

Answers

NAME ______________ DATE ________ PERIOD ____

10-3 Study Guide and Intervention

Solving Quadratic Equations by Completing the Square

Find the Square Root An equation such as $x^2 - 4x + 4 = 5$ can be solved by taking the square root of each side.

Example 1 **Solve $x^2 - 2x + 1 = 9$. Round to the nearest tenth if necessary.**

$$
\begin{aligned}
x^2 - 2x + 1 &= 9 \\
(x - 1)^2 &= 9 \\
\sqrt{(x - 1)^2} &= \sqrt{9} \\
|x - 1| &= \sqrt{9} \\
x - 1 &= \pm 3 \\
x - 1 + 1 &= \pm 3 + 1 \\
x &= 1 \pm 3
\end{aligned}
$$

$x = 1 + 3$ or $x = 1 - 3$
$= 4$ $\quad = -2$

The solution set is $\{-2, 4\}$.

Example 2 **Solve $x^2 - 4x + 4 = 5$. Round to the nearest tenth if necessary.**

$$
\begin{aligned}
x^2 - 4x + 4 &= 5 \\
(x - 2)^2 &= 5 \\
\sqrt{(x - 2)^2} &= \sqrt{5} \\
|x - 2| &= \sqrt{5} \\
x - 2 &= \pm\sqrt{5} \\
x - 2 + 2 &= \pm\sqrt{5} + 2 \\
x &= 2 \pm \sqrt{5}
\end{aligned}
$$

Use a calculator to evaluate each value of x.

$x = 2 + \sqrt{5}$ or $x = 2 - \sqrt{5}$
≈ 4.2 $\quad \approx -0.2$

The solution set is $\{-0.2, 4.2\}$.

Exercises

Solve each equation by taking the square root of each side. Round to the nearest tenth if necessary.

1. $x^2 + 4x + 4 = 9$
−5, 1

2. $m^2 + 12m + 36 = 1$
−7, −5

3. $r^2 - 6r + 9 = 16$
−1, 7

4. $x^2 - 2x + 1 = 25$
−4, 6

5. $x^2 - 8x + 16 = 5$
1.8, 6.2

6. $x^2 - 10x + 25 = 8$
2.2, 7.8

7. $c^2 - 4c + 4 = 7$
−0.6, 4.6

8. $p^2 + 16p + 64 = 3$
−9.7, −6.3

9. $x^2 + 8x + 16 = 9$
−7, −1

10. $x^2 + 6x + 9 = 4$
−5, −1

11. $a^2 + 8a + 16 = 10$
−7.2, −0.8

12. $y^2 - 12y + 36 = 5$
3.8, 8.2

13. $x^2 + 10x + 25 = 1$
−6, −4

14. $y^2 + 14y + 49 = 6$
−9.4, −4.6

15. $m^2 - 8m + 16 = 2$
2.6, 5.4

16. $x^2 + 12x + 36 = 10$
−9.2, −2.8

17. $a^2 - 14a + 49 = 3$
5.3, 8.7

18. $y^2 + 8y + 16 = 7$
−6.6, −1.4

Lesson 10-3

NAME ______________ DATE ________ PERIOD ____

10-3 Study Guide and Intervention (continued)

Solving Quadratic Equations by Completing the Square

Complete the Square Since few quadratic expressions are perfect square trinomials, the method of **completing the square** can be used to solve some quadratic equations. Use the following steps to complete the square for a quadratic expression of the form $ax^2 + bx$.

Step 1	Find $\frac{b}{2}$.
Step 2	Find $\left(\frac{b}{2}\right)^2$.
Step 3	Add $\left(\frac{b}{2}\right)^2$ to $ax^2 + bx$.

Example **Solve $x^2 + 6x + 3 = 10$ by completing the square.**

$x^2 + 6x + 3 = 10$	Original equation
$x^2 + 6x + 3 - 3 = 10 - 3$	Subtract 3 from each side.
$x^2 + 6x = 7$	Simplify.
$x^2 + 6x + 9 = 7 + 9$	Since $\left(\frac{6}{2}\right)^2 = 9$, add 9 to each side.
$(x + 3)^2 = 16$	Factor $x^2 + 6x + 9$.
$x + 3 = \pm 4$	Take the square root of each side.
$x = -3 \pm 4$	Simplify.

$x = -3 + 4$ or $x = -3 - 4$
$= 1$ $\quad = -7$

The solution set is $\{-7, 1\}$.

Exercises

Solve each equation by completing the square. Round to the nearest tenth if necessary.

1. $t^2 - 4t + 3 = 0$
1, 3

2. $y^2 + 10y = -9$
−1, −9

3. $y^2 - 8y - 9 = 0$
−1, 9

4. $x^2 - 6x = 16$
−2, 8

5. $p^2 - 4p - 5 = 0$
−1, 5

6. $x^2 - 12x = 9$
−0.7, 12.7

7. $c^2 + 8c = 20$
−10, 2

8. $p^2 = 2p + 1$
−0.4, 2.4

9. $x^2 + 20x + 11 = -8$
−19, −1

10. $x^2 - 1 = 5x$
−0.2, 5.2

11. $a^2 = 22a + 23$
−1, 23

12. $m^2 - 8m = -7$
1, 7

13. $x^2 + 10x = 24$
−12, 2

14. $a^2 - 18a = 19$
−1, 19

15. $b^2 + 16b = -16$
−14.9, −1.1

16. $4x^2 = 24 + 4x$
−2, 3

17. $2m^2 + 4m + 2 = 8$
−3, 1

18. $4k^2 = 40k + 44$
−1, 11

NAME ______ DATE ______ PERIOD ______

10-3 Skills Practice

Solving Quadratic Equations by Completing the Square

Solve each equation by taking the square root of each side. Round to the nearest tenth if necessary.

1. $c^2 - 12c + 36 = 4$ **4, 8**

2. $w^2 - 10w + 25 = 16$ **1, 9**

3. $b^2 + 16b + 64 = 9$ **−11, −5**

4. $y^2 + 2y + 1 = 3$ **−2.7, 0.7**

5. $r^2 + 4r + 4 = 7$ **−4.6, 0.6**

6. $a^2 - 8a + 16 = 12$ **0.5, 7.5**

Find the value of *c* that makes each trinomial a perfect square.

7. $g^2 + 6g + c$ **9**

8. $y^2 + 4y + c$ **4**

9. $a^2 - 14a + c$ **49**

10. $n^2 - 2n + c$ **1**

11. $s^2 - 18s + c$ **81**

12. $p^2 + 20p + c$ **100**

Solve each equation by completing the square. Round to the nearest tenth if necessary.

13. $x^2 + 4x - 12 = 0$ **2, −6**

14. $v^2 - 8v + 15 = 0$ **3, 5**

15. $q^2 + 6q = 7$ **−7, 1**

16. $r^2 - 2r = 15$ **−3, 5**

17. $m^2 - 14m + 30 = 6$ **2, 12**

18. $b^2 + 12b + 21 = 10$ **−11, −1**

19. $z^2 - 4z + 1 = 0$ **0.3, 3.7**

20. $y^2 - 6y + 4 = 0$ **0.8, 5.2**

21. $r^2 - 8r + 10 = 0$ **1.6, 6.4**

22. $p^2 - 2p = 5$ **−1.4, 3.4**

23. $2a^2 + 20a = -2$ **−9.9, −0.1**

24. $0.5g^2 + 8g = -7$ **−15.1, −0.9**

Lesson 10-3

NAME ______ DATE ______ PERIOD ______

10-3 Practice (Average)

Solving Quadratic Equations by Completing the Square

Solve each equation by taking the square root of each side. Round to the nearest tenth if necessary.

1. $b^2 - 14b + 49 = 64$ **−1, 15**

2. $s^2 + 16s + 64 = 100$ **−18, 2**

3. $h^2 - 8h + 16 = 15$ **0.1, 7.9**

4. $a^2 + 6a + 9 = 27$ **−8.2, 2.2**

5. $p^2 - 20p + 100 = 28$ **4.7, 15.3**

6. $u^2 + 10u + 25 = 90$ **−14.5, 4.5**

Find the value of *c* that makes each trinomial a perfect square.

7. $t^2 - 24t + c$ **144**

8. $b^2 + 28b + c$ **196**

9. $y^2 + 40y + c$ **400**

10. $m^2 + 3m + c$ $\mathbf{\frac{9}{4}}$

11. $g^2 - 9g + c$ $\mathbf{\frac{81}{4}}$

12. $v^2 - v + c$ $\mathbf{\frac{1}{4}}$

Solve each equation by completing the square. Round to the nearest tenth if necessary.

13. $w^2 - 14w + 24 = 0$ **2, 12**

14. $p^2 + 12p = 13$ **−13, 1**

15. $s^2 - 30s + 56 = -25$ **3, 27**

16. $v^2 + 8v + 9 = 0$ **−6.6, −1.4**

17. $t^2 - 10t + 6 = -7$ **1.5, 8.5**

18. $n^2 + 18n + 50 = 9$ **−15.3, −2.7**

19. $3u^2 + 15u - 3 = 0$ **−5.2, 0.2**

20. $4c^2 - 72 = 24c$ **−2.2, 8.2**

21. $0.9a^2 + 5.4a - 4 = 0$ $\mathbf{-6\frac{2}{3}, \frac{2}{3}}$

22. $0.4h^2 + 0.8h = 0.2$ **−2.2, 0.2**

23. $\frac{1}{2}x^2 - \frac{1}{2}x - 10 = 0$ **−4, 5**

24. $\frac{1}{4}x^2 + \frac{3}{2}x - 2 = 0$ **−7.1, 1.1**

BUSINESS For Exercises 25 and 26, use the following information.

Jaime owns a business making decorative boxes to store jewelry, mementos, and other valuables. The function $y = x^2 + 50x + 1800$ models the profit y that Jaime has made in month x for the first two years of his business.

25. Write an equation representing the month in which Jaime's profit is $2400.
$\mathbf{x^2 + 50x + 1800 = 2400}$

26. Use completing the square to find out in which month Jaime's profit is $2400.
the tenth month

27. PHYSICS From a height of 256 feet above a lake on a cliff, Mikaela throws a rock out over the lake. The height H of the rock t seconds after Mikaela throws it is represented by the equation $H = -16t^2 + 32t + 256$. To the nearest tenth of a second, how long does it take the rock to reach the lake below? (*Hint:* Replace H with 0.) **5.1 s**

Answers

NAME ______________ DATE ________ PERIOD ____

10-3 Reading to Learn Mathematics

Solving Quadratic Equations by Completing the Square

Pre-Activity **How did ancient mathematicians use squares to solve algebraic equations?**

Read the introduction to Lesson 10-3 at the top of page 539 in your textbook.

To solve the problem, how many "units" would Al-Khwarizmi have added to each side of the equation? 16

Reading the Lesson

1. Draw a line under each quadratic equation that you could solve by taking the square root of each side.

<u>$x^2 + 6x + 9 = 100$</u>	$x^2 - 14x + 40 = 25$	<u>$x^2 - 16x + 64 = 26$</u>
$x^2 - 20x + 80 = 16$	$x^2 + 10x + 36 = 49$	<u>$x^2 - 12x + 36 = 6$</u>

2. How can you tell whether it is possible to solve a quadratic equation by taking the square root of each side?

Sample answer: Check to be sure that all terms that contain the variable are on the same side of the equation. Next, check whether the quadratic expression is a perfect square. Finally, check that the number on the side that contains no variables is greater than or equal to 0.

3. Explain how to find what number is needed for the ■ in order to make $x^2 - 20x + ■$ a perfect square.

Find one half of −20, which is −10, and square it. The result, which is 100, is the required number.

4. To solve $3x^2 - 6x = 54$ by completing the square, why does it help first to divide both sides by 3?

Sample answer: If you divide both sides by 3, the coefficient of x^2 will be 1. It is then easy to use the coefficient of x to decide what number you need to add to both sides to make the left side a perfect square trinomial.

Helping You Remember

5. The method of completing the square might be easier to remember if you can connect it to what you know about perfect square trinomials. How is completing the square related to the method you use to determine whether a trinomial is a perfect square trinomial?

Sample answer: If the first and last terms of a trinomial are perfect squares, you *multiply* the product of their *square roots by 2* to get the middle term. In completing the square, you check that the coefficient of x^2 is 1. Then you divide the coefficient of the x term by 2 and square the result to get the third term.

Lesson 10-3

NAME ______________ DATE ________ PERIOD ____

10-3 Enrichment

Parabolas Through Three Given Points

If you know two points on a straight line, you can find the equation of the line. To find the equation of a parabola, you need three points on the curve.

Here is how to approximate an equation of the parabola through the points (0, −2), (3, 0), and (5, 2).

Use the general equation $y = ax^2 + bx + c$. By substituting the given values for x and y, you get three equations.

(0, −2): $-2 = c$
(3, 0): $0 = 9a + 3b + c$
(5, 2): $2 = 25a + 5b + c$

First, substitute −2 for c in the second and third equations. Then solve those two equations as you would any system of two equations. Multiply the second equation by 5 and the third equation by −3.

$0 = 9a + 3b - 2$ (Multiply by 5.) $\quad 0 = 45a + 15b - 10$
$0 = 25a + 5b - 2$ (Multiply by −3.) $\quad -6 = -75a - 15b + 6$

$-6 = -30a \quad - 4$

$a = \frac{1}{15}$

To find b, substitute $\frac{1}{15}$ for a in either the second or third equation.

$0 = 9\left(\frac{1}{15}\right) + 3b - 2$

$b = \frac{7}{15}$

The equation of a parabola through the three points is

$y = \frac{1}{15}x^2 + \frac{7}{15}x - 2.$

Find the equation of a parabola through each set of three points.

1. (1, 5), (0, 6), (2, 3)
$y = -\frac{1}{2}x^2 - \frac{1}{2}x + 6$

2. (−5, 0), (0, 0), (8, 100)
$y = \frac{25}{26}x^2 + \frac{125}{26}x$

3. (4, −4), (0, 1), (3, −2)
$y = -\frac{1}{4}x^2 - \frac{1}{4}x + 6$

4. (1, 3), (6, 0), (0, 0)
$y = -\frac{3}{5}x^2 + \frac{18}{5}x$

5. (2, 2), (5, −3), (0, −1)
$y = -\frac{19}{30}x^2 + \frac{83}{30}x - 1$

6. (0, 4), (4, 0), (−4, 4)
$y = -\frac{1}{8}x^2 - \frac{1}{2}x + 4$

NAME ______ DATE ______ PERIOD ______

10-4 Study Guide and Intervention

Solving Quadratic Equations by Using the Quadratic Formula

Quadratic Formula To solve the standard form of the quadratic equation, $ax^2 + bx + c = 0$, use the **Quadratic Formula**.

Quadratic Formula	the formula $x = \frac{-b \pm \sqrt{b^2 - 4ac}}{2a}$ that gives the solutions of $ax^2 + bx + c = 0$, where $a \neq 0$

Example 1 **Solve $x^2 + 2x = 3$ by using the Quadratic Formula.**

Rewrite the equation in standard form.

$x^2 + 2x = 3$ Original equation

$x^2 + 2x - 3 = 3 - 3$ Subtract 3 from each side.

$x^2 + 2x - 3 = 0$ Simplify.

Now let $a = 1$, $b = 2$, and $c = -3$ in the Quadratic Formula.

$x = \frac{-b \pm \sqrt{b^2 - 4ac}}{2a}$

$= \frac{-2 \pm \sqrt{(2)^2 - 4(1)(-3)}}{2(1)}$

$= \frac{-2 \pm \sqrt{16}}{2}$

$x = \frac{-2 + 4}{2}$ or $x = \frac{-2 - 4}{2}$

$= 1$ $= -3$

The solution set is $\{-3, 1\}$.

Example 2 **Solve $x^2 - 6x - 2 = 0$ by using the Quadratic Formula. Round to the nearest tenth if necessary.**

For this equation $a = 1$, $b = -6$, and $c = -2$.

$x = \frac{-b \pm \sqrt{b^2 - 4ac}}{2a}$

$= \frac{6 \pm \sqrt{(-6)^2 - 4(1)(-2)}}{2(1)}$

$= \frac{6 \pm \sqrt{44}}{2}$

$x = \frac{6 + \sqrt{44}}{2}$ or $x = \frac{6 - \sqrt{44}}{2}$

≈ 6.3 ≈ -0.3

The solution set is $\{-0.3, 6.3\}$.

Exercises

Solve each equation by using the Quadratic Formula. Round to the nearest tenth if necessary.

1. $x^2 - 3x + 2 = 0$ **1, 2**
2. $m^2 - 8m = -16$ **4**
3. $16r^2 - 8r = -1$ $\mathbf{\frac{1}{4}}$
4. $x^2 + 5x = 6$ **−6, 1**
5. $3x^2 + 2x = 8$ $\mathbf{-2, \frac{4}{3}}$
6. $8x^2 - 8x - 5 = 0$ **−0.4, 1.4**
7. $-4c^2 + 19c = 21$ $\mathbf{\frac{7}{4}, 3}$
8. $2p^2 + 6p = 5$ **−3.7, 0.7**
9. $48x^2 + 22x - 15 = 0$ $\mathbf{-\frac{5}{6}, \frac{3}{8}}$
10. $8x^2 - 4x = 24$ $\mathbf{-\frac{3}{2}, 2}$
11. $2p^2 + 5p = 8$ **−3.6, 1.1**
12. $8y^2 + 9y - 4 = 0$ **−1.5, 0.3**
13. $2x^2 + 9x + 4 = 0$ $\mathbf{-4, -\frac{1}{2}}$
14. $8y^2 + 17y + 2 = 0$ $\mathbf{-2, -\frac{1}{8}}$
15. $3z^2 + 5z - 2 = 0$ $\mathbf{-2, \frac{1}{3}}$
16. $-2x^2 + 8x + 4 = 0$ **−0.4, 4.4**
17. $a^2 + 3a = 2$ **−3.6, 0.6**
18. $2y^2 - 6y + 4 = 0$ **1, 2**

Lesson 10-4

NAME ______ DATE ______ PERIOD ______

10-4 Study Guide and Intervention (continued)

Solving Quadratic Equations by Using the Quadratic Formula

The Discriminant In the Quadratic Formula, $x = \frac{-b \pm \sqrt{b^2 - 4ac}}{2a}$, the expression under the radical sign, $b^2 - 4ac$, is called the **discriminant**. The discriminant can be used to determine the number of real roots for a quadratic equation.

Case 1: $b^2 - 4ac < 0$	Case 2: $b^2 - 4ac = 0$	Case 3: $b^2 - 4ac > 0$
no real roots	one real root	two real roots

Example **State the value of the discriminant for each equation. Then determine the number of real roots.**

a. $12x^2 + 5x = 4$

Write the equation in standard form.

$12x^2 + 5x = 4$ Original equation

$12x^2 + 5x - 4 = 4 - 4$ Subtract 4 from each side.

$12x^2 + 5x - 4 = 0$ Simplify.

Now find the discriminant.

$b^2 - 4ac = (5)^2 - 4(12)(-4)$

$= 217$

Since the discriminant is positive, the equation has two real roots.

b. $2x^2 + 3x = -4$

$2x^2 + 3x = -4$ Original equation

$2x^2 + 3x + 4 = -4 + 4$ Add 4 to each side.

$2x^2 + 3x + 4 = 0$ Simplify.

$b^2 - 4ac = (3)^2 - 4(2)(4)$

$= -23$

Since the discriminant is negative, the equation has no real roots.

Exercises

State the value of the discriminant for each equation. Then determine the number of real roots of the equation.

1. $3x^2 + 2x - 3 = 0$ **40, 2 real roots**
2. $3n^2 - 7n - 8 = 0$ **145, 2 real roots**
3. $2d^2 - 10d - 9 = 0$ **172, 2 real roots**
4. $4x^2 = x + 4$ **65, 2 real roots**
5. $3x^2 - 13x = 10$ **289, 2 real roots**
6. $6x^2 - 10x + 10 = 0$ **−140, no real roots**
7. $2k^2 - 20 = -k$ **161, 2 real roots**
8. $6p^2 = -11p - 40$ **−839, no real roots**
9. $9 - 18x + 9x^2 = 0$ **0, 1 real root**
10. $12x^2 + 9 = -6x$ **−396, no real roots**
11. $9a^2 = 81$ **2916, 2 real roots**
12. $16y^2 + 16y + 4 = 0$ **0, 1 real roots**
13. $8x^2 + 9x = 2$ **145, 2 real roots**
14. $4a^2 - 4a + 4 = 3$ **0, 1 real root**
15. $3b^2 - 18b = -14$ **156, 2 real roots**

NAME ______________________ DATE __________ PERIOD _____

10-4 Skills Practice

Solving Quadratic Equations by Using the Quadratic Formula

Solve each equation by using the Quadratic Formula. Round to the nearest tenth if necessary.

1. $u^2 - 49 = 0$ **−7, 7**

2. $n^2 - n - 20 = 0$ **−4, 5**

3. $s^2 - 5s - 36 = 0$ **−4, 9**

4. $b^2 + 11b + 30 = 0$ **−6, −5**

5. $c^2 - 7c = -3$ **0.5, 6.5**

6. $p^2 + 4p = -1$ **−3.7, −0.3**

7. $a^2 - 9a + 22 = 0$ **∅**

8. $x^2 + 6x + 3 = 0$ **−5.4, −0.6**

9. $2x^2 + 5x - 7 = 0$ $-3\frac{1}{2}, 1$

10. $2h^2 - 3h = -1$ $\frac{1}{2}, 1$

11. $2p^2 + 5p + 4 = 0$ **∅**

12. $2g^2 + 7g = 9$ $-4\frac{1}{2}, 1$

13. $3t^2 + 2t - 3 = 0$ **−1.4, 0.7**

14. $3x^2 - 7x - 6 = 0$ $-\frac{2}{3}, 3$

State the value of the discriminant for each equation. Then determine the number of real roots of the equation.

15. $q^2 + 4q + 3 = 0$
4; 2 real roots

16. $m^2 + 2m + 1 = 0$
0; 1 real root

17. $a^2 - 4a + 10 = 0$
−24; no real roots

18. $w^2 - 6w + 7 = 0$
8; 2 real roots

19. $z^2 - 2z - 7 = 0$
32; 2 real roots

20. $y^2 - 10y + 25 = 0$
0; 1 real root

21. $2d^2 + 5d - 8 = 0$
89; 2 real roots

22. $2s^2 + 6s + 12 = 0$
−60; no real roots

23. $2u^2 - 4u + 10 = 0$
−64; no real roots

24. $3h^2 + 7h + 3 = 0$
13; 2 real roots

Lesson 10-4

NAME ______________________ DATE __________ PERIOD _____

10-4 Practice (Average)

Solving Quadratic Equations by Using the Quadratic Formula

Solve each equation by using the Quadratic Formula. Round to the nearest tenth if necessary.

1. $g^2 + 2g - 3 = 0$ **−3, 1**

2. $a^2 + 8a + 7 = 0$ **−7, −1**

3. $v^2 - 4v + 6 = 0$ **∅**

4. $d^2 - 6d + 7 = 0$ **1.6, 4.4**

5. $2z^2 + 9z - 5 = 0$ $-5, \frac{1}{2}$

6. $2r^2 + 12r + 10 = 0$ **−5, −1**

7. $2b^2 - 9b = -12$ **∅**

8. $2h^2 - 5h = 12$ $-1\frac{1}{2}, 4$

9. $3p^2 + p = 4$ $-1\frac{1}{3}, 1$

10. $3m^2 - 1 = -8m$ **−2.8, 0.1**

11. $4y^2 + 7y = 15$ $-3, 1\frac{1}{4}$

12. $1.6n^2 + 2n + 2.5 = 0$ **∅**

13. $4.5k^2 + 4k - 1.5 = 0$
−1.2, 0.3

14. $\frac{1}{2}c^2 + 2c + \frac{3}{2} = 0$
−3, −1

15. $3w^2 - \frac{3}{4}w = \frac{1}{2}$
−0.3, 0.6

State the value of the discriminant for each equation. Then determine the number of real roots of the equation.

16. $a^2 + 8a + 16 = 0$
0; 1 real root

17. $c^2 + 3c + 12 = 0$
−39; no real roots

18. $2w^2 + 12w = -7$
88; 2 real roots

19. $2u^2 + 15u = -30$
−15; no real roots

20. $4n^2 + 9 = 12n$
0; 1 real root

21. $3g^2 - 2g = 3.5$
46; 2 real roots

22. $2.5k^2 + 3k - 0.5 = 0$
14; 2 real roots

23. $\frac{3}{4}d^2 - 3d = -4$
−3; no real roots

24. $\frac{1}{4}s^2 = -s - 1$
0; 1 real root

CONSTRUCTION For Exercises 25 and 26, use the following information.

A roofer tosses a piece of roofing tile from a roof onto the ground 30 feet below. He tosses the tile with an initial downward velocity of 10 feet per second.

25. Write an equation to find how long it takes the tile to hit the ground. Use the model for vertical motion, $H = -16t^2 + vt + h$, where H is the height of an object after t seconds, v is the initial velocity, and h is the initial height. (*Hint:* Since the object is thrown down, the initial velocity is negative.) $H = -16t^2 - 10t + 30$

26. How long does it take the tile to hit the ground? **about 1.1 s**

27. PHYSICS Lupe tosses a ball up to Quyen, waiting at a third-story window, with an initial velocity of 30 feet per second. She releases the ball from a height of 6 feet. The equation $h = -16t^2 + 30t + 6$ represents the height h of the ball after t seconds. If the ball must reach a height of 25 feet for Quyen to catch it, does the ball reach Quyen? Explain. (*Hint:* Substitute 25 for h and use the discriminant.)
No; the discriminant, −316, is negative, so there is no solution.

NAME ______________________ DATE __________ PERIOD _____

10-4 Reading to Learn Mathematics

Solving Quadratic Equations by Using the Quadratic Formula

Pre-Activity **How can the Quadratic Formula be used to solve problems involving population trends?**

Read the introduction to Lesson 10-4 at the top of page 546 in your textbook.

Your teacher asks you to predict when 17% of the population will consist of people born outside the United States. What equation should you use to make the prediction?

$17 = 0.006t^2 - 0.080t + 5.281$

Reading the Lesson

1. Suppose you want to solve $12x^2 + 7x = 15$ using the Quadratic Formula.

   a. What should you do first?

   Rewrite the equation in the form $ax^2 + bx + c = 0$.

   b. What are the values you need to substitute for a, b, and c in the Quadratic Formula?

   $a = 12$, $b = 7$, and $c = -15$

   c. Apply the Quadratic Formula using the above values, but do not solve the equation.

   $$x = \frac{-7 \pm \sqrt{7^2 - 4(12)(-15)}}{2(12)}$$

2. a. You can use the discriminant to determine the number of real roots for a quadratic equation. What is the discriminant?

   The discriminant is the expression under the radical sign in the Quadratic Formula, $b^2 - 4ac$.

   b. Complete the statements below so that each statement is true.

   When the value of the discriminant is ___zero___, there is one real root.

   When the value of the discriminant is ___positive___, there are two real roots.

   When the value of the discriminant is ___negative___, there are no real roots.

Helping You Remember

3. To help remember the methods for solving a quadratic equation, explain how you would choose the best method for solving a quadratic equation $ax^2 + bx + c = 0$.

   Sample answer: Use graphing for approximate solutions. Use the Quadratic Formula for exact solutions. Use factoring when the factors are easy to determine. Use completing the square when b is an even number.

NAME ______________________ DATE __________ PERIOD _____

10-4 Enrichment

Mechanical Constructions of Parabolas

A given line and a point determine a parabola. Here is one way to construct the curve.

Use a right triangle ABC (or a stiff piece of rectangular cardboard).

Place one leg of the triangle on the given line d. Fasten one end of a string with length BC at the given point F and the other end to the triangle at point B.

Put the tip of a pencil at point P and keep the string tight.

As you move the triangle along the line d, the point of your pencil will trace a parabola.

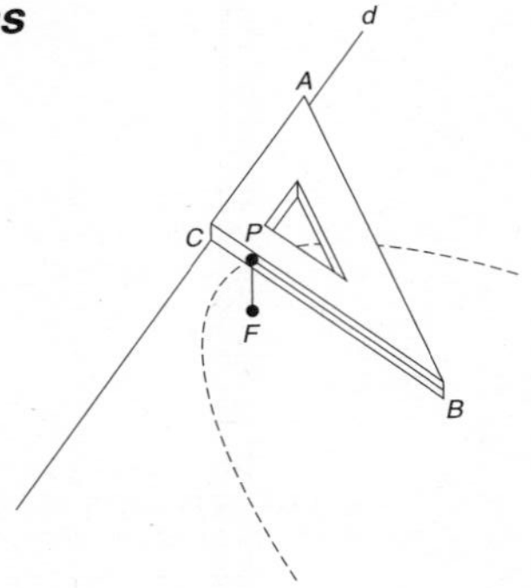

Draw the parabola determined by line d and point F.

1. 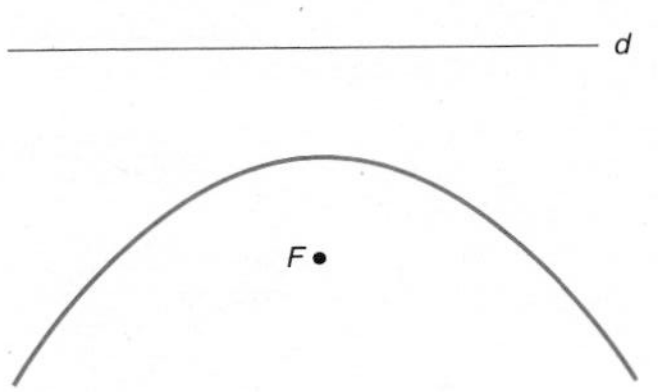

2. 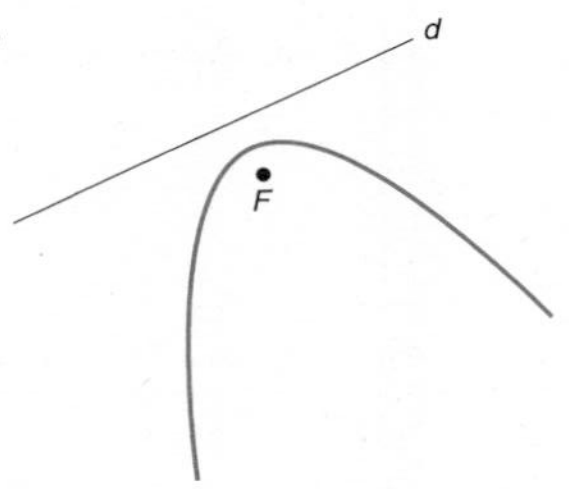

3. 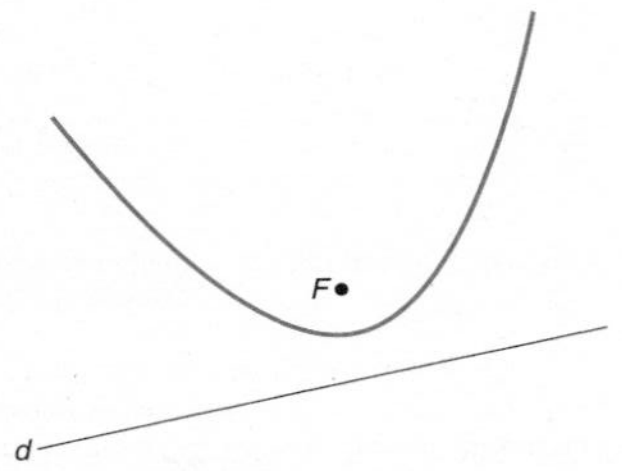

4. 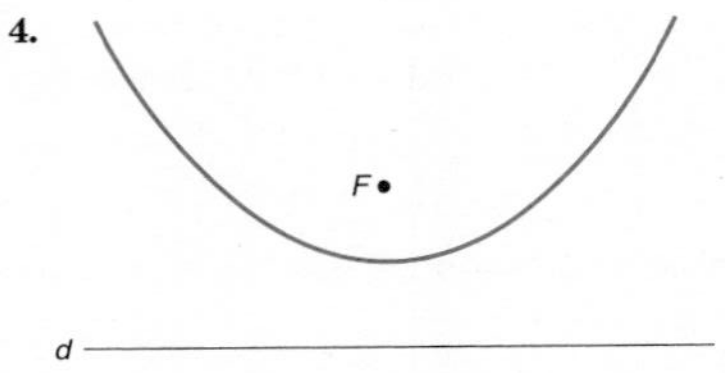

5. Use your drawings to complete this conclusion. The greater the distance of point F from line d, the wider the opening of the parabola.

NAME ______________________ DATE __________ PERIOD ____

10-5 Study Guide and Intervention

Exponential Functions

Graph Exponential Functions

Exponential Function	a function defined by an equation of the form $y = ax$, where $a > 0$ and $a \neq 1$

You can use values of x to find ordered pairs that satisfy an exponential function. Then you can use the ordered pairs to graph the function.

Example 1 **Graph $y = 3^x$. State the y-intercept.**

x	y
−2	$\frac{1}{9}$
−1	$\frac{1}{3}$
0	1
1	3
2	9

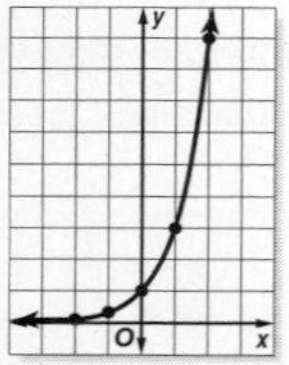

The y-intercept is 1.

Example 2 **Graph $y = \left(\frac{1}{4}\right)^x$. Use the graph to determine the approximate value of $\left(\frac{1}{4}\right)^{-0.5}$.**

x	y
−2	16
−1	4
0	1
1	$\frac{1}{4}$
2	$\frac{1}{16}$

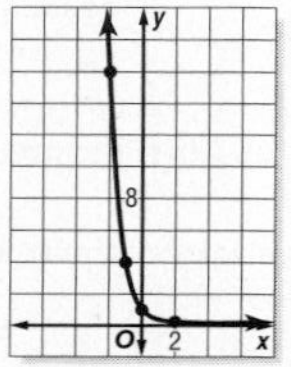

The value of $\left(\frac{1}{4}\right)^{-0.5}$ is about 2.

Exercises

1. Graph $y = 0.3^x$. State the y-intercept. Then use the graph to determine the approximate value of $0.3^{-1.5}$. Use a calculator to confirm the value. 1; about 6

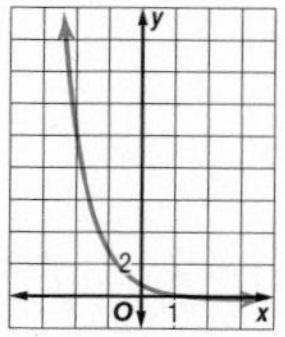

Graph each function. State the y-intercept.

2. $y = 3^x + 1$ 2

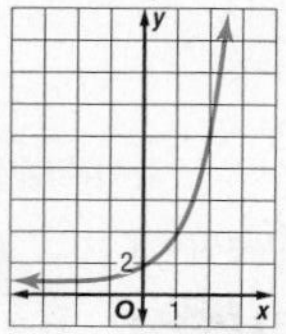

3. $y = \left(\frac{1}{3}\right)^x + 1$ 2

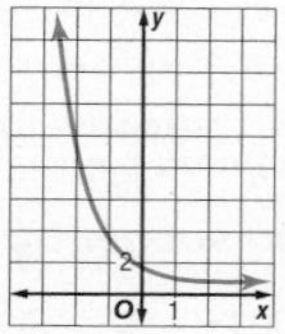

4. $y = \left(\frac{1}{2}\right)^x - 2$ −1

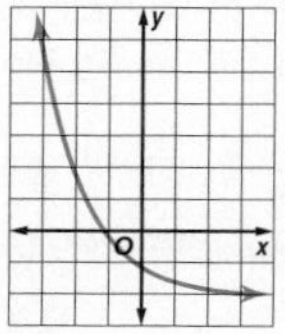

Lesson 10-5

NAME ______________________ DATE __________ PERIOD ____

10-5 Study Guide and Intervention *(continued)*

Exponential Functions

Identify Exponential Behavior It is sometimes useful to know if a set of data is exponential. One way to tell is to observe the shape of the graph. Another way is to observe the pattern in the set of data.

Example **Determine whether the set of data displays exponential behavior.**

x	0	2	4	6	8	10
y	64	32	16	8	4	2

Method 1: Graph the Data

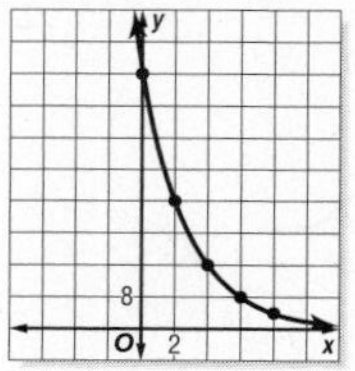

The graph shows rapidly decreasing values of y as x increases. This is characteristic of exponential behavior.

Method 2: Look for a Pattern
The domain values increase by regular intervals of 2, while the range values have a common factor of $\frac{1}{2}$. Since the domain values increase by regular intervals and the range values have a common factor, the data are probably exponential.

Exercises

Determine whether the data in each table display exponential behavior. Explain why or why not.

1.

x	0	1	2	3
y	5	10	15	20

No; the domain values are at regular intervals, and the range values have a common difference 5.

2.

x	0	1	2	3
y	3	9	27	81

Yes; the domain values are at regular intervals, and the range values have a common factor 3.

3.

x	−1	1	3	5
y	32	16	8	4

Yes; the domain values are at regular intervals, and the range values have a common factor $\frac{1}{2}$.

4.

x	−1	0	1	2	3
y	3	3	3	3	3

No; the domain values are at regular intervals, but the range values do not change.

5.

x	−5	0	5	10
y	1	0.5	0.25	0.125

Yes; the domain values are at regular intervals, and the range values have a common factor 0.5.

6.

x	0	1	2	3	4
y	$\frac{1}{3}$	$\frac{1}{9}$	$\frac{1}{27}$	$\frac{1}{81}$	$\frac{1}{243}$

Yes; the domain values are at regular intervals, and the range values have a common factor $\frac{1}{3}$.

NAME ______________________ DATE ____________ PERIOD _____

10-5 Skills Practice

Exponential Functions

Graph each function. State the y-intercept. Then use the graph to determine the approximate value of the given expression. Use a calculator to confirm the value.

1. $y = 2^x$; $2^{2.3}$

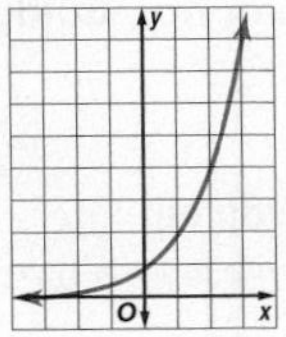

1; 4.9

2. $y = \left(\frac{1}{3}\right)^x$; $\left(\frac{1}{3}\right)^{-1.6}$

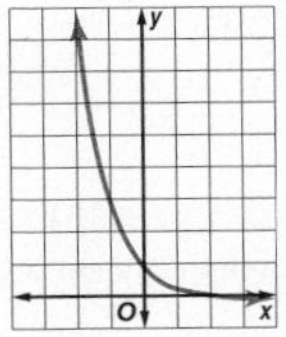

1; 5.8

Graph each function. State the y-intercept.

3. $y = 3(2^x)$

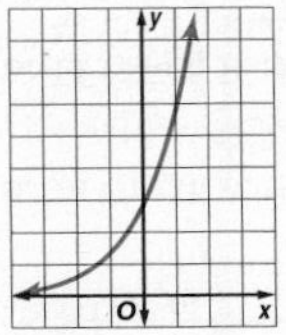

3

4. $y = 3^x + 2$

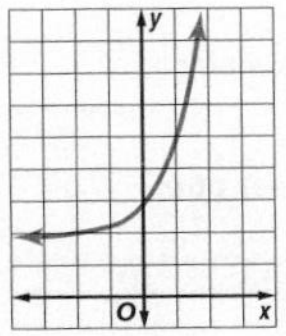

3

Determine whether the data in each table display exponential behavior. Explain why or why not.

5.

x	−3	−2	−1	0
y	9	12	15	18

No; the domain values are at regular intervals and the range values have a common difference 3.

6.

x	0	5	10	15
y	20	10	5	2.5

Yes; the domain values are at regular intervals and the range values have a common factor 0.5.

7.

x	4	8	12	16
y	20	40	80	160

Yes; the domain values are at regular intervals and the range values have a common factor 2.

8.

x	50	30	10	−10
y	90	70	50	30

No; the domain values are at regular intervals and the range values have a common difference 20.

Lesson 10-5

NAME ______________________ DATE ____________ PERIOD _____

10-5 Practice (Average)

Exponential Functions

Graph each function. State the y-intercept. Then use the graph to determine the approximate value of the given expression. Use a calculator to confirm the value.

1. $y = \left(\frac{1}{10}\right)^x$; $\left(\frac{1}{10}\right)^{-0.5}$ **1; 3.2**

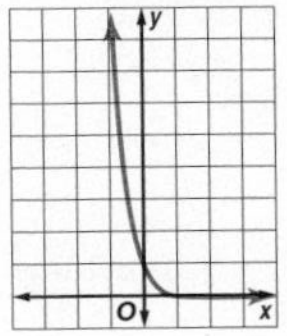

2. $y = 3^x$; $3^{1.9}$ **1; 8.1**

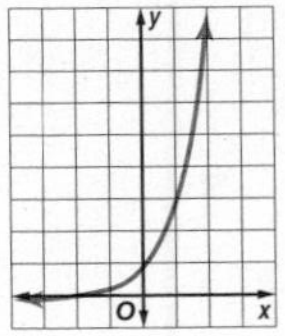

3. $y = \left(\frac{1}{4}\right)^x$; $\left(\frac{1}{4}\right)^{-1.4}$ **1; 7.0**

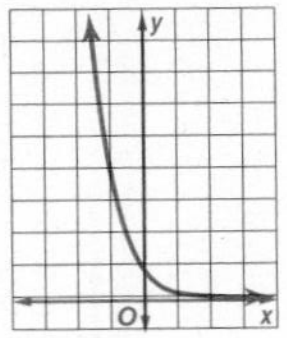

Graph each function. State the y-intercept.

4. $y = 4(2^x) + 1$ **5**

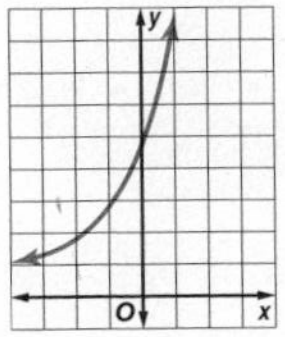

5. $y = 2(2^x - 1)$ **0**

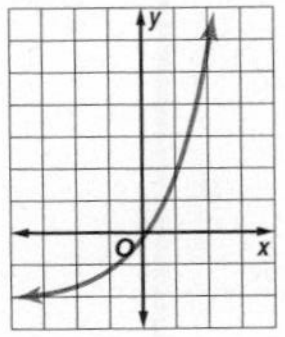

6. $y = 0.5(3^x - 3)$ **−1**

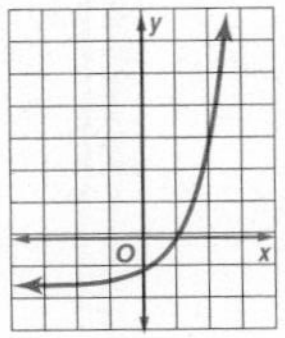

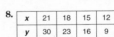

Determine whether the data in each table display exponential behavior. Explain why or why not.

7.

x	2	5	8	11
y	480	120	30	7.5

Yes; the domain values are at regular intervals and the range values have a common factor 0.25.

8.

x	21	18	15	12
y	30	23	16	9

No; the domain values are at regular intervals and the range values have a common difference 7.

9. LEARNING Ms. Klemperer told her English class that each week students tend to forget one sixth of the vocabulary words they learned the previous week. Suppose a student learns 60 words. The number of words remembered can be described by the function $W(x) = 60\left(\frac{5}{6}\right)^x$, where x is the number of weeks that pass. How many words will the student remember after 3 weeks? **about 35**

10. BIOLOGY Suppose a certain cell reproduces itself in four hours. If a lab researcher begins with 50 cells, how many cells will there be after one day, two days, and three days? (*Hint:* Use the exponential function $y = 50(2^x)$.) **3200 cells; 204,800 cells; 13,107,200 cells**

Answers

NAME ______________ DATE ________ PERIOD ____

10-5 Reading to Learn Mathematics

Exponential Functions

Pre-Activity **How can exponential functions be used in art?**

Read the introduction to Lesson 10-5 at the top of page 554 in your textbook.

If Mr. Warther had carved a ninth layer of pliers, how many pliers would he have carved?

2^9 or 512 pliers

Reading the Lesson

1. The graphs of two exponential functions of the form $y = a^x$ are shown below.

A.

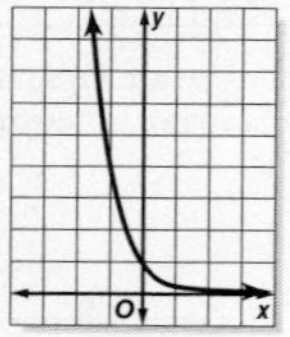

B.

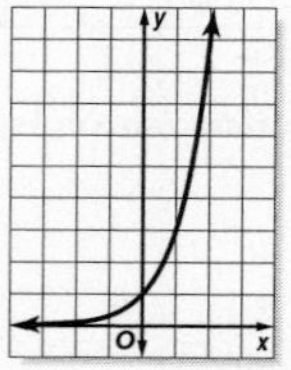

a. In Graph A, the value of a is greater than __0__ and less than __1__. The y values decrease as the x values __increase__.

b. In Graph B, the value of a is greater than __1__. The y values __increase__ as the x values increase.

2. a. When you look for a pattern of exponential behavior in a set of data, what is the pattern you are looking for?

Values of x (domain values) that are at regular intervals and values of y (range values) that have a common factor.

b. If a set of data has a negative common factor, does it display exponential behavior?

No; the common factor needs to be greater than 0 and not equal to 1.

Helping You Remember

3. What comparisons can you make between the quadratic function $y = x^2$ and the exponential function $y = 2^x$ to help remember the differences between quadratic and exponential functions?

Sample answer: In the quadratic function, the variable is the base and the exponent is a number; in the exponential function, the variable is the exponent and the base is a number.

NAME ______________ DATE ________ PERIOD ____

10-5 Enrichment

Writing Expressions of Area in Factored Form

Write an expression in factored form for the area A of the shaded region in each figure below.

1.

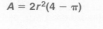

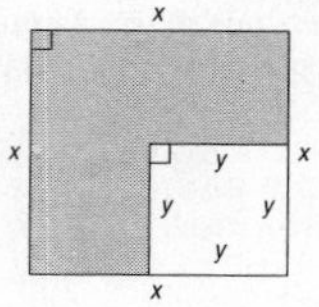

$A = (x + y)(x - y)$

2.

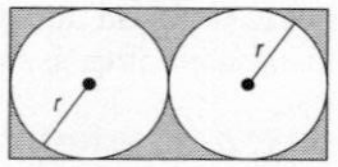

$A = 2r^2(4 - \pi)$

3.

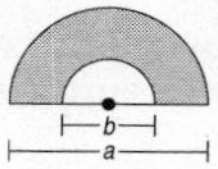

$A = \frac{\pi}{8}(a + b)(a - b)$

4.

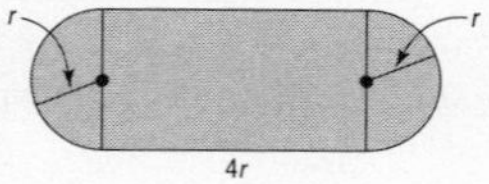

$A = r^2(8 + \pi)$

5.

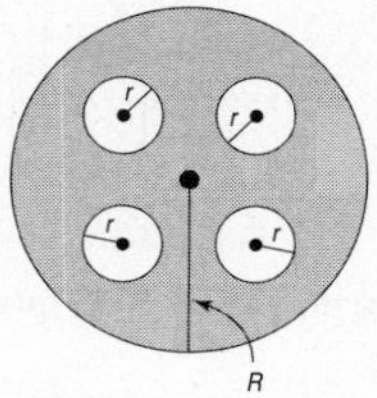

$A = \pi(R + 2r)(R - 2r)$

6.

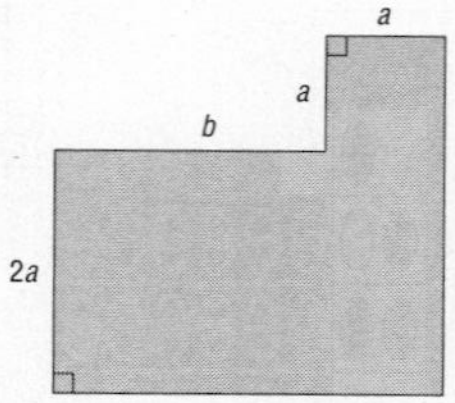

$A = a(3a + 2b)$

7.

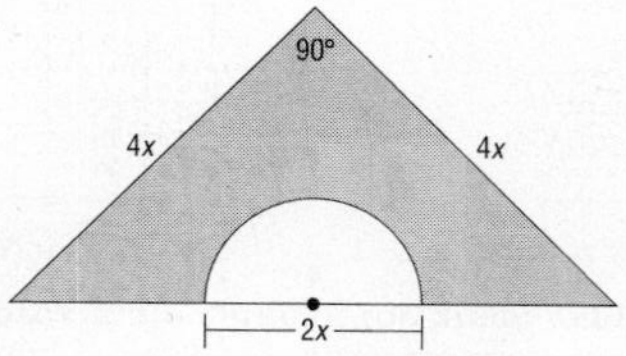

$A = x^2\left(8 - \frac{\pi}{2}\right)$

8.

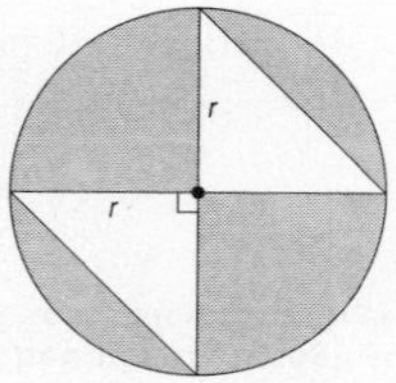

$A = r^2(\pi - 1)$

NAME ______________ DATE ________ PERIOD ____

10-6 Study Guide and Intervention

Growth and Decay

Exponential Growth Population increases and growth of monetary investments are examples of **exponential growth**. This means that an initial amount increases at a steady rate over time.

Exponential Growth	The general equation for exponential growth is $y = C(1 + r)^t$. • y represents the final amount. • C represents the initial amount. • r represents the rate of change expressed as a decimal. • t represents time.

Example 1 **POPULATION The population of Johnson City in 1995 was 25,000. Since then, the population has grown at an average rate of 3.2% each year.**

a. Write an equation to represent the population of Johnson City since 1995.

The rate 3.2% can be written as 0.032.

$y = C(1 + r)^t$
$y = 25{,}000(1 + 0.032)^t$
$y = 25{,}000(1.032)^t$

b. According to the equation, what will the population of Johnson City be in the year 2005?

In 2005, t will equal 2005 − 1995 or 10.

Substitute 10 for t in the equation from part a.

$y = 25{,}000(1.032)^{10}$ $t = 10$
$\approx 34{,}256$

In 2005, the population of Johnson City will be about 34,256.

Example 2 **INVESTMENT The Garcias have $12,000 in a savings account. The bank pays 3.5% interest on savings accounts, compounded monthly. Find the balance in 3 years.**

The rate 3.5% can be written as 0.035.

The special equation for compound interest is $A = P\left(1 + \frac{r}{n}\right)^{nt}$, where A represents the balance, P is the initial amount, r represents the annual rate expressed as a decimal, n represents the number of times the interest is compounded each year, and t represents the number of years the money is invested.

$A = P\left(1 + \frac{r}{n}\right)^{nt}$

$A = 12{,}000\left(1 + \frac{0.035}{12}\right)^{36}$

$A \approx 12{,}000(1.00292)^{36}$
$A \approx 13{,}328.09$

In three years, the balance of the account will be $13,328.09.

Exercises

1. **POPULATION** The population of the United States has been increasing at an average annual rate of 0.91%. If the population of the United States was about 284,905,400 in the year 2001, predict the U. S. population in the year 2005. **Source:** U. S. Census Bureau **about 295,418,375**

2. **INVESTMENT** Determine the amount of an investment of $2500 if it is invested at in interest rate of 5.25% compounded monthly for 4 years. **$3082.78**

3. **POPULATION** It is estimated that the population of the world is increasing at an average annual rate of 1.3%. If the population of the world was about 6,167,007,000 in the year 2001, predict the world population in the year 2010. **Source:** U. S. Census Bureau **about 6,927,227,483**

4. **INVESTMENT** Determine the amount of an investment of $100,000 if it is invested at an interest rate of 5.2% compounded quarterly for 12 years. **$185,888.87**

Lesson 10-6

NAME ______________ DATE ________ PERIOD ____

10-6 Study Guide and Intervention *(continued)*

Growth and Decay

Exponential Decay Radioactive decay and depreciation are examples of **exponential decay**. This means that an initial amount decreases at a steady rate over a period of time.

Exponential Decay	The general equation for exponential decay is $y = C(1 - r)^t$. • y represents the final amount. • C represents the initial amount. • r represents the rate of decay expressed as a decimal. • t represents time.

Example **DEPRECIATION The original price of a tractor was $45,000. The value of the tractor decreases at a steady rate of 12% per year.**

a. Write an equation to represent the value of the tractor since it was purchased.

The rate 12% can be written as 0.12.

$y = C(1 - r)^t$ General equation for exponential decay
$y = 45{,}000(1 - 0.12)^t$ $C = 45{,}000$ and $r = 0.12$
$y = 45{,}000(0.88)^t$ Simplify.

b. What is the value of the tractor in 5 years?

$y = 45{,}000(0.88)^t$ Equation for decay from part a
$y = 45{,}000(0.88)^5$ $t = 5$
$y \approx 23{,}747.94$ Use a calculator.

In 5 years, the tractor will be worth about $23,747.94.

Exercises

1. **POPULATION** The population of Bulgaria has been decreasing at an annual rate of 1.3%. If the population of Bulgaria was about 7,797,000 in the year 2000, predict its population in the year 2010. **Source:** U. S. Census Bureau **about 6,841,000**

2. **DEPRECIATION** Carl Gossell is a machinist. He bought some new machinery for about $125,000. He wants to calculate the value of the machinery over the next 10 years for tax purposes. If the machinery depreciates at the rate of 15% per year, what is the value of the machinery (to the nearest $100) at the end of 10 years? **about $24,600**

3. **ARCHAEOLOGY** The *half-life* of a radioactive element is defined as the time that it takes for one-half a quantity of the element to decay. Radioactive Carbon-14 is found in all living organisms and has a half-life of 5730 years. Consider a living organism with an original concentration of Carbon-14 of 100 grams.
   - **a.** If the organism lived 5730 years ago, what is the concentration of Carbon-14 today? **50 g**
   - **b.** If the organism lived 11,460 years ago, determine the concentration of Carbon-14 today. **25 g**

4. **DEPRECIATION** A new car costs $32,000. It is expected to depreciate 12% each year for 4 years and then depreciate 8% each year thereafter. Find the value of the car in 6 years. **about $16,242.63**

NAME ______________ DATE ________ PERIOD ____

10-6 Skills Practice
Growth and Decay

POPULATION For Exercises 1 and 2, use the following information.
The population of New York City increased from 7,322,564 in 1990 to 8,008,278 in 2000. The annual rate of population increase for the period was about 0.9%. **Source:** www.nyc.gov

1. Write an equation for the population t years after 1990. $P = 7{,}322{,}564(1.009)^t$

2. Use the equation to predict the population of New York City in 2010. **about 8,760,000**

SAVINGS For Exercises 3 and 4, use the following information.
The Fresh and Green Company has a savings plan for its employees. If an employee makes an initial contribution of $1000, the company pays 8% interest compounded quarterly.

3. If an employee participating in the plan withdraws the balance of the account after 5 years, how much will be in the account? **$1485.95**

4. If an employee participating in the plan withdraws the balance of the account after 35 years, how much will be in the account? **$15,996.47**

5. **HOUSING** Mr. and Mrs. Boyce bought a house for $96,000 in 1995. The real estate broker indicated that houses in their area are appreciating at an average annual rate of 4%. If the appreciation remains steady at this rate, what will be the value of the Boyce's home in 2005? **about $142,103**

MANUFACTURING For Exercises 6 and 7, use the following information.
Zeller Industries bought a piece of weaving equipment for $60,000. It is expected to depreciate at an average rate of 10% per year.

6. Write an equation for the value of the piece of equipment after t years. $E = 60{,}000(0.90)^t$

7. Find the value of the piece of equipment after 6 years. **about $31,886**

8. **FINANCES** Kyle saved $500 from a summer job. He plans to spend 10% of his savings each week on various forms of entertainment. At this rate, how much will Kyle have left after 15 weeks? **$102.95**

9. **TRANSPORTATION** Tiffany's mother bought a car for $9000 five years ago. She wants to sell it to Tiffany based on a 15% annual rate of depreciation. At this rate, how much will Tiffany pay for the car? **about $3993**

Lesson 10-6

NAME ______________ DATE ________ PERIOD ____

10-6 Practice (Average)
Growth and Decay

COMMUNICATIONS For Exercises 1 and 2, use the following information.
Commercial non-music radio stations increased at an average annual rate of 3.1% from 1996 to 2000. Commercial radio stations in this format numbered 1262 in 1996.
Source: M Street Corporation, Nashville, TN

1. Write an equation for the number of radio stations for t years after 1996. $R = 1262(1.031)^t$

2. If the trend continues, predict the number of radio stations in this format for the year 2006. **about 1713 stations**

3. **INVESTMENTS** Determine the amount of an investment if $500 is invested at an interest rate of 4.25% compounded quarterly for 12 years. **$830.41**

4. **INVESTMENTS** Determine the amount of an investment if $300 is invested at an interest rate of 6.75% compounded semiannually for 20 years. **$1131.73**

5. **HOUSING** The Greens bought a condominium for $110,000 in 2000. If its value appreciates at an average rate of 6% per year, what will the value be in 2005? **about $147,205**

DEFORESTATION For Exercises 6 and 7, use the following information.
During the 1990s, the forested area of Guatemala decreased at an average rate of 1.7%.
Source: www.worldbank.org

6. If the forested area in Guatemala in 1990 was about 34,400 square kilometers, write an equation for the forested area for t years after 1990. $C = 34{,}400(0.983)^t$

7. If this trend continues, predict the forested area in 2015. **about 22,400 km²**

8. **BUSINESS** A piece of machinery valued at $25,000 depreciates at a steady rate of 10% yearly. What will the value of the piece of machinery be after 7 years? **about $11,957**

9. **TRANSPORTATION** A new car costs $18,000. It is expected to depreciate at an average rate of 12% per year. Find the value of the car in 8 years. **about $6473**

10. **POPULATION** The population of Osaka, Japan declined at an average annual rate of 0.05% for the five years between 1995 and 2000. If the population of Osaka was 11,013,000 in 2000 and it continues to decline at the same rate, predict the population in 2050. **about 10,741,000**

NAME ______________ DATE ________ PERIOD ____

10-6 Reading to Learn Mathematics

Growth and Decay

Pre-Activity How can exponential growth be used to predict future sales?

Read the introduction to Lesson 10-6 at the top of page 561 in your textbook.

Suppose you want to predict the amount of money an average household will spend on restaurant meals in the year 2005. What number should be substituted for t? 11

Reading the Lesson

Match an equation to each situation, and then indicate whether the situation is an example of exponential growth or decay.

1. A coin had a value of \$1.17 in 1995. Its value has been increasing at a rate of 9% per year. A; growth

   A. $y = 1.17(1.09)^t$ **B.** $y = 1.17(0.91)^t$

2. A business owner has just paid \$6000 for a computer. It depreciates at a rate of 22% per year. How much will it be worth in 5 years? B; decay

   A. $A = 6000(1.22)^5$ **B.** $A = 6000(0.78)^5$

3. A city had a population of 14,358 residents in 1999. Since then, its population has been decreasing at a rate of about 5.5% per year. B; decay

   A. $A = 14{,}358(1.055)^t$ **B.** $A = 14{,}358(0.945)^t$

4. Gina deposited \$1500 in an account that pays 4% interest compounded quarterly. What will be the worth of the account in 2 years if she makes no deposits and no withdrawals? B; growth

   A. $A = 1500(1.02)^2$ **B.** $A = 1500(1.02)^8$

Helping You Remember

5. How can you use what you know about raising a number to the 0 power to help you remember what C represents in the exponential growth equation $A = C(1 + r)^t$ and the exponential decay equation $A = C(1 - r)^t$?

   Sample answer: The initial amount is the amount before any time has passed, that is, when $t = 0$. When $t = 0$, $C(1 + r)^t = C(1 + r)^0 = C(1) = C$ and $C(1 - r)^t = C(1 - r)^0 = C(1) = C$. So C represents the initial amount.

Lesson 10-6

NAME ______________ DATE ________ PERIOD ____

10-6 Enrichment

Curious Circles

Two circles can be arranged in four ways: one circle can be inside the other, they can be separate, they can overlap, or they can coincide.

In how many ways can a given number of circles be either separate or inside each other? (The situations in which the circles overlap or coincide are not counted here.)

For 3 circles, there are 4 different possibilities.

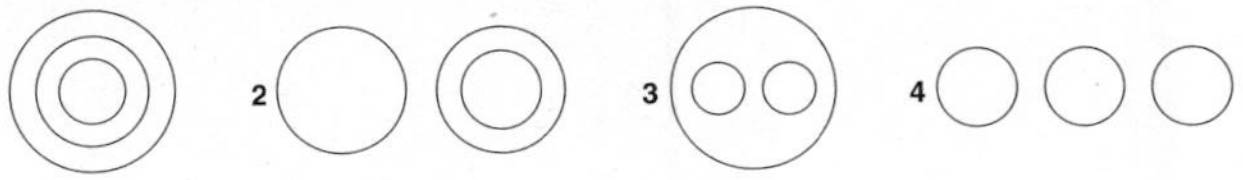

Solve each problem. Make drawings to show your answers.

1. Show the different ways in which 2 circles can be separate or inside each other. How many ways are there? two ways

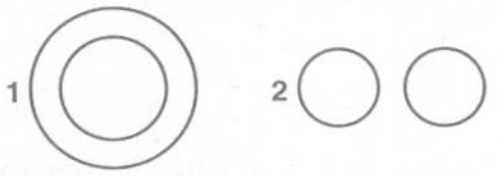

2. Show the different ways for 4 circles. How many ways are there? nine ways

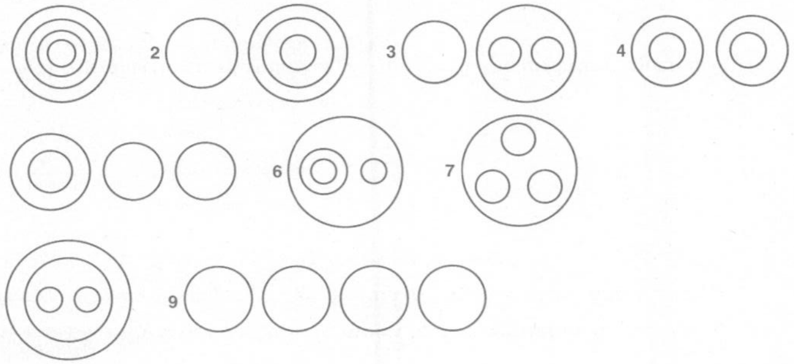

3. Use your answer for Exercise 2 to show that the number of ways for 5 circles is at least 18. First, draw an extra circle next to each of the ways for 4 circles. Then draw a circle around each of the ways for 4 circles.

4. Find the number of ways for 5 circles. Show your drawings on a separate sheet of paper. 20 ways

Answers

NAME ______________________ DATE __________ PERIOD ____

10-7 Study Guide and Intervention

Geometric Sequences

Geometric Sequences A **geometric sequence** is a sequence in which each term after the nonzero first term is found by multiplying the previous term by a constant called the **common ratio**.

Geometric Sequence	a sequence of numbers of the form $a, ar, ar^2, ar^3, \ldots$, where $a \neq 0$, and $r \neq 0$ or 1	**Example:** 1, 2, 4, 8, 16, ...

Example 1 **Determine whether each sequence is geometric.**

a. 3, 6, 9, 12, 15, ...
In this sequence, each term is found by adding 3 to the previous term. The sequence is arithmetic and not geometric.

b. 1, 4, 16, 64, ...
In this sequence, each term is found by multiplying the previous term by 4. The sequence is geometric.

Example 2 **Find the next three terms in each geometric sequence.**

a. 8, −4, 2, −1, ...
The common factor is $\frac{-4}{8}$ or $-\frac{1}{2}$. Use this information to find the next three terms.

$(-1)\left(-\frac{1}{2}\right) = \frac{1}{2}$
$\frac{1}{2}\left(-\frac{1}{2}\right) = -\frac{1}{4}$
$\left(-\frac{1}{4}\right)\left(-\frac{1}{2}\right) = \frac{1}{8}$

The next three terms are $\frac{1}{2}$, $-\frac{1}{4}$, and $\frac{1}{8}$.

b. 7, 14, 28, 56, ...
The common ratio is $\frac{14}{7}$ or 2. Use this information to find the next three terms.

56(2) = 112
112(2) = 224
224(2) = 448

The next three terms are 112, 224, 448.

Exercises

Determine whether each sequence is geometric.

1. 2, 4, 6, 8, 10, ... **no**
2. 2, 4, 8, 16, 32, ... **yes**
3. −10, −5, −2.5, −1.25, ... **yes**
4. 100, 400, 1600, 6400, ... **yes**
5. $\frac{1}{2}, \frac{1}{3}, \frac{1}{4}, \frac{1}{5}, \ldots$ **no**
6. $\frac{1}{3}, \frac{1}{9}, \frac{1}{27}, \frac{1}{81}, \ldots$ **yes**

Find the next three terms in each geometric sequence.

7. 100, 300, 900, 2700, ... **8100, 24,300, 72,900**
8. $\frac{1}{2}, \frac{1}{4}, \frac{1}{8}, \frac{1}{16}, \ldots$ $\frac{1}{32}, \frac{1}{64}, \frac{1}{128}$
9. 80, 40, 20, 10, ... $5, \frac{5}{2}, \frac{5}{4}$

Find the nth term of each geometric sequence.

10. $a_1 = 5, n = 6, r = 3$ **1215**
11. $a_1 = 3, n = 5, r = 4$ **768**
12. $a_1 = -5, n = 7, r = -2$ **−320**

NAME ______________________ DATE __________ PERIOD ____

10-7 Study Guide and Intervention *(continued)*

Geometric Sequences

Geometric Means A missing term or terms between two nonconsecutive terms in a geometric sequence are called **geometric means**. In the sequence 10, 20, 40, 80, ..., the geometric mean between 10 and 40 is 20. You can use the formula $a_n = a_1 \cdot r^{n-1}$ to find a geometric mean.

Example **Find the geometric mean in the sequence 6, ___, 150.**

In the sequence, $a_1 = 6$ and $a_3 = 150$. To find a_2, you must first find r.

$a_n = a_1 \cdot r^{n-1}$	Formula for the nth term of a geometric sequence
$a_3 = a_1 \cdot r^{3-1}$	$n = 3$
$150 = 6 \cdot r^2$	$a_3 = 150$ and $a_1 = 6$
$\frac{150}{6} = \frac{6r^2}{6}$	Divide each side by 6.
$25 = r^2$	Simplify.
$\pm 5 = r$	Take the square root of each side.

If $r = 5$, the geometric mean is 6(5) or 30. If $r = -5$, the geometric mean is 6(−5) or −30. Therefore the geometric mean is 30 or −30.

Exercises

Find the geometric means in each sequence.

1. 4, ___, 16 **±8**
2. 12, ___, 108 **±36**
3. −8, ___, −128 **±32**
4. 180, ___, 20 **±60**
5. −2, ___, −98 **±14**
6. 600, ___, 150 **±300**
7. $\frac{1}{4}$, ___, $\frac{1}{16}$ $\pm\frac{1}{8}$
8. $\frac{1}{2}$, ___, $\frac{1}{32}$ $\pm\frac{1}{8}$
9. $-\frac{3}{5}$, ___, $-\frac{15}{16}$ $\pm\frac{3}{4}$
10. 14, ___, $\frac{2}{7}$ **±2**
11. $\frac{5}{8}$, ___, 10 $\pm\frac{5}{2}$
12. $-\frac{2}{3}$, ___, −54 **±6**
13. 2.3, ___, 9.2 **±4.6**
14. −137.7, ___, −15.3 **±45.9**
15. −5.1, ___, −127.5 **±25.5**
16. $\frac{3}{8}$, ___, $\frac{3}{32}$ $\pm\frac{3}{16}$
17. −15, ___, $-\frac{3}{5}$ **±3**
18. 8, ___, 320,000 **±1600**

NAME ______________________ DATE __________ PERIOD _____

10-7 Skills Practice

Geometric Sequences

Determine whether each sequence is geometric.

1. 9, 17, 25, 33, … **no**

2. 4, 12, 36, 108, … **yes**

3. −320, −80, −20, −5, … **yes**

4. −75, −60, −45, −30, … **no**

5. 64, −32, 16, −8, … **yes**

6. 26.5, 21, 15.5, 10, … **no**

Find the next three terms in each geometric sequence.

7. 2, −4, 8, −16, …
32, −64, 128

8. −2, −6, −18, −54, …
−162, −486, −1458

9. −960, 480, −240, 120, …
−60, 30, −15

10. 7290, 2430, 810, 270, …
90, 30, 10

11. −32, −16, −8, −4, …
−2, −1, −0.5

12. 6144, 1536, 384, 96, …
24, 6, 1.5

Find the *n*th term of each geometric sequence.

13. $a_1 = 2, n = 4, r = -2$ **−16**

14. $a_1 = 3, n = 5, r = 2$ **48**

15. $a_1 = 6, n = 3, r = 8$ **384**

16. $a_1 = -5, n = 4, r = 9$ **−3645**

17. $a_1 = 10, n = 3, r = 12$ **1440**

18. $a_1 = 4, n = 4, r = -8$ **−2048**

Find the geometric means in each sequence.

19. 8, ___, 72 **±24**

20. 75, ___, 3 **±15**

21. −2, ___, −128 **±16**

22. −112, ___, −7 **±28**

23. 324, ___, 4 **±36**

24. 1.5, ___, 24 **±6**

NAME ______________________ DATE __________ PERIOD _____

10-7 Practice (Average)

Geometric Sequences

Determine whether each sequence is geometric.

1. 3, 12, 48, 192, … **yes**

2. 2, 17, 32, 47, … **no**

3. −200, −135, −70, −5, … **no**

4. −220, −110, −55, −27.5, … **yes**

5. −992, 248, −62, 15.5, … **yes**

6. −20, −50, −125, −312.5, … **yes**

Find the next three terms in each geometric sequence.

7. −4, −20, −100, −500, …
−2500, −12,500, −62,500

8. 7, −21, 63, −189, …
567, −1701, 5103

9. −6250, 1250, −250, 50 …
−10, 2, −0.4

10. 50, 70, 98, 137.2, …
192.08, 268.912, 376.4768

11. 5, −4, 3.2, −2.56 …
2.048, −1.6384, 1.31072

12. $\frac{1}{4}, \frac{1}{6}, \frac{1}{9}, \frac{2}{27}, \ldots$
$\mathbf{\frac{4}{81}, \frac{8}{243}, \frac{16}{729}}$

Find the *n*th term of each geometric sequence.

13. $a_1 = 6, n = 5, r = 3$
486

14. $a_1 = -9, n = 6, r = 2$
−288

15. $a_1 = 8, n = 3, r = -11$
968

16. $a_1 = 50, n = 7, r = 3$
36,450

17. $a_1 = -5, n = 3, r = 1.5$
−11.25

18. $a_1 = 7, n = 5, r = 0.5$
0.4375

Find the geometric means in each sequence.

19. 4, ___, 256 **±32**

20. −8, ___, −392 **±56**

21. 2, ___, 0.5 **±1**

22. −20, ___, −1.25 **±5**

23. $\frac{3}{4}$, ___, $\frac{3}{64}$ $\mathbf{\pm\frac{3}{16}}$

24. $\frac{1}{2}$, ___, $\frac{2}{25}$ $\mathbf{\pm\frac{1}{5}}$

MAGAZINE SUBSCRIPTIONS For Exercises 25 and 26, use the following information.
The manager of a teen magazine wants to increase subscriptions by at least 6% each year for the next three years to keep the company operating at a profit. Subscriptions for 2003 are 17,500.

25. Determine the minimum number of subscriptions the sales team must sell for the years 2004, 2005, and 2006. **18,550; 19,663; 20,843**

26. Suppose the manager wants to increase the subscriptions to 35,000. How long will it take to reach this goal if subscriptions increase at 6% per year? **about 12 yr**

NAME ______________ DATE ________ PERIOD ____

10-7 Reading to Learn Mathematics

Geometric Sequences

Pre-Activity **How can a geometric sequence be used to describe a bungee jump?**

Read the introduction to Lesson 10-7 at the top of page 567 in your textbook.

How can you find the distance of the fifth bounce?

Multiply $33\frac{3}{4}$ ft by $\frac{3}{4}$.

Reading the Lesson

1. Suppose you are given the first three terms of a geometric sequence and want to find the next three terms.

a. What should you do to find the common ratio?

Divide the second term of the sequence by the first, or divide the third term by the second.

b. What should you do after you find the common ratio?

Beginning with the third term of the sequence, multiply by the common ratio. Multiply the resulting product by the common ratio, and repeat this step with the new product.

2. Suppose you are asked to give an example of a geometric sequence. Are there any restrictions on the terms of the sequence or the common ratio r? Explain.

Yes; the sequence cannot begin with 0, and the common ratio cannot be equal to 0 or 1.

3. You can use the formula for the nth term of a geometric sequence to find any term in the sequence. What information do you need in order to use the formula?

You need to know the first term of the sequence, the common ratio, and where the term you are interested in falls in the sequence.

4. Consider the geometric sequence 3, 6, 12, 24, 48, ... How many geometric means are there for each pair of terms? What are they?

a. 3 and 12 **one; 6**

b. 3 and 24 **two; 6 and 12**

Helping You Remember

5. To remember an idea, it can help if you explain it to someone else. Suppose a friend thinks that the formula for the nth term of a geometric sequence should be $a_n = a_1r^n$ rather than $a_n = a_1r^{n-1}$. How would you explain why it should be $a_n = a_1r^{n-1}$?

Sample answer: The sequence starts with a_1. The second term is $a_2 = a_1r^1$. The third term is $a_3 = a_1r^2$, and so on. The exponent for r is one less than the term number. So $a_n = a_1r^{n-1}$.

NAME ______________ DATE ________ PERIOD ____

10-7 Enrichment

Convergence, Divergence, and Limits

Imagine that a runner runs a mile from point A to point B. But, this is not an ordinary race! In the first minute, he runs one-half mile, reaching point C. In the next minute, he covers one-half the remaining distance, or $\frac{1}{4}$ mile, reaching point D. In the next minute he covers one-half the remaining distance, or $\frac{1}{8}$ mile, reaching point E.

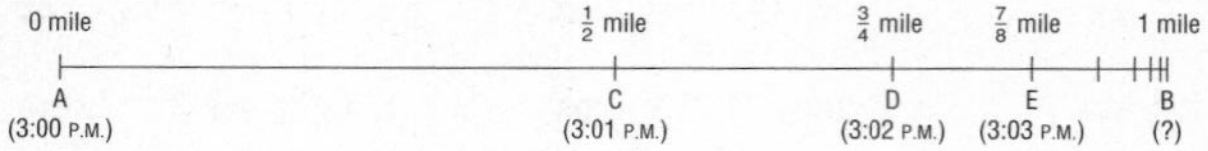

In this strange race, the runner approaches closer and closer to point B, but never gets there. However close he is to B, there is still some distance remaining, and in the next minute he can cover only half of that distance. This race can be modeled by the infinite sequence

$\frac{1}{2}, \frac{3}{4}, \frac{7}{8}, \frac{15}{16}, \ldots$.

The terms of the sequence get closer and closer to 1. An infinite sequence that gets arbitrarily close to some number is said to **converge** to that number. The number is the limit of the sequence.

Not all infinite sequences converge. Those that do not are called **divergent**.

Write C if the sequence converges and D if it diverges. If the sequence converges, make a reasonable guess for its limit.

1. 2, 4, 6, 8, 10, ... **D**

2. 0, 3, 0, 3, 0, 3, ... **D**

3. $1, \frac{1}{2}, \frac{1}{3}, \frac{1}{4}, \frac{1}{5}, \ldots$ **C, 0**

4. 0.9, 0.99, 0.999, 0.9999, ... **C, 1**

5. −5, 5, −5, 5, −5, 5, ... **D**

6. 0.1, 0.2, 0.3, 0.4, ... **D**

7. $2\frac{1}{4}, 2\frac{3}{4}, 2\frac{7}{8}, 2\frac{15}{16}, \ldots$ **C, 3**

8. $6, 5\frac{1}{2}, 5\frac{1}{3}, 5\frac{1}{4}, 5\frac{1}{5}, \ldots$ **C, 5**

9. 1, 4, 9, 16, 25, ... **D**

10. $-1, -\frac{1}{2}, -\frac{1}{3}, -\frac{1}{4}, -\frac{1}{5}, \ldots$ **C, 0**

11. Create one convergent sequence and one divergent sequence. Give the limit for your convergent sequence. **Answers will vary. Sample answer:**

$1, \frac{1}{3}, \frac{1}{9}, \frac{1}{27}, \frac{1}{81}, \ldots$ convergent, 0

1, 5, 25, 125, 625, ... divergent

Chapter 10 Assessment Answer Key

Form 1
Page 621

1. C
2. B
3. C
4. A
5. D
6. D
7. B
8. D
9. A
10. B

Page 622

11. B
12. C
13. A
14. C
15. B
16. C
17. A
18. D
19. B
20. C

B: 1 real root

Form 2A
Page 623

1. B
2. B
3. D
4. C
5. A
6. B
7. C
8. D
9. D

(continued on the next page)

Answers

Chapter 10 Assessment Answer Key

Form 2A *(continued)*
Page 624

10. A
11. C
12. A
13. A
14. B
15. A
16. B
17. D
18. C
19. D
20. B

B: $x = 1$

Form 2B
Page 625

1. A
2. B
3. C
4. D
5. A
6. D
7. B
8. A
9. C

Page 626

10. D
11. A
12. B
13. C
14. D
15. B
16. D
17. C
18. A
19. B
20. C

B: −16, 16

Chapter 10 Assessment Answer Key

Form 2C

Page 627

1. 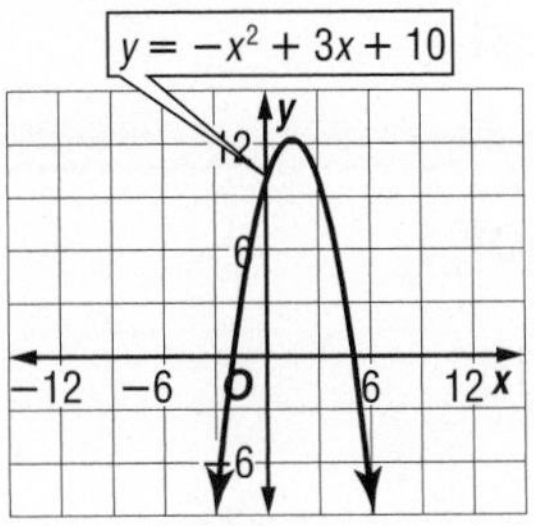

2. 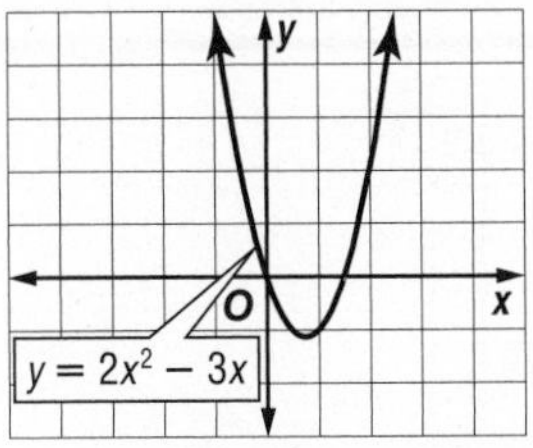

3. $x = 2$; $(2, -5)$; minimum

4. 3

5. $0 < x < 1$, $5 < x < 6$

6. -3, $6 < x < 7$

7. −2.2, 4.2

8. −23, 3

9. −4, 2.5

10. 0.8, 11.2

11. $-\frac{1}{3}, \frac{3}{5}$

12. −14.6, −1.4

13. yes

14. 8192, −65,536, 524,288

Page 628

15. 148; 2 real roots

16. 0; 1 real root

17. about 201 lb

18. 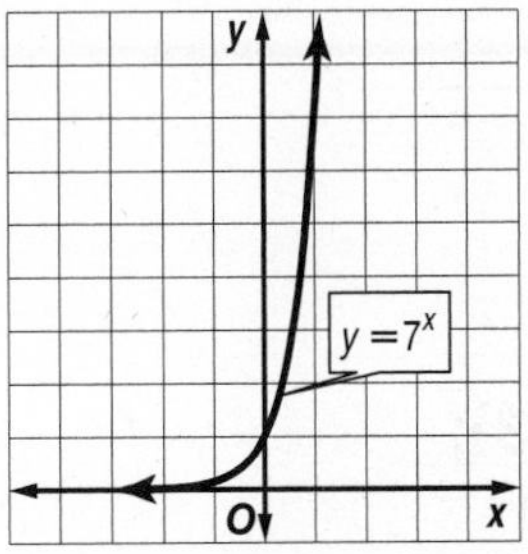

1

19. 3.2

20. No; the domain values are at regular intervals, but the range values do not have a positive common factor.

21. Yes; the domain values at regular intervals and the range values have a common factor 3.

22. about \$1434.67

23. about \$14,797.81

24. −1029

25. 48 or −48

B: about −1.2 and −0.1

Chapter 10 Assessment Answer Key

Form 2D

Page 629

1. 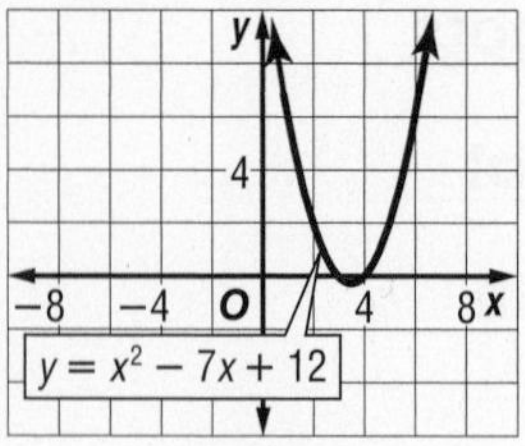

2. 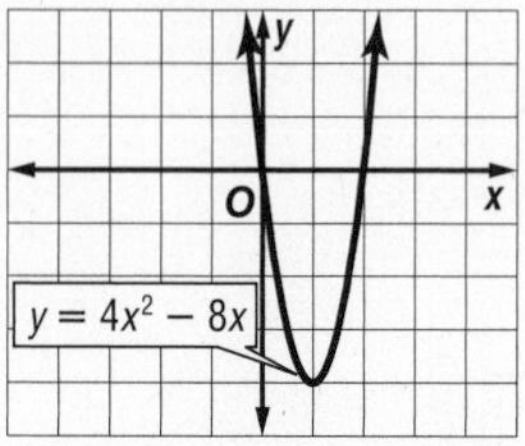

3. $x = 1$; (1, −3); maximum

4. 1, 3

5. $-1 < x < 0$, $2 < x < 3$

6. $-3 < x < -2$, 5

7. −1, 19

8. −8.9, −1.1

9. $-6, \frac{3}{2}$

10. −14.2, −0.8

11. $-\frac{3}{4}, \frac{2}{3}$

12. 1.8, 12.2

13. no

14. 3888, −23,328, 139,968

Page 630

15. −56; no real roots

16. 0; 1 real root

17. about 185 lb

18. 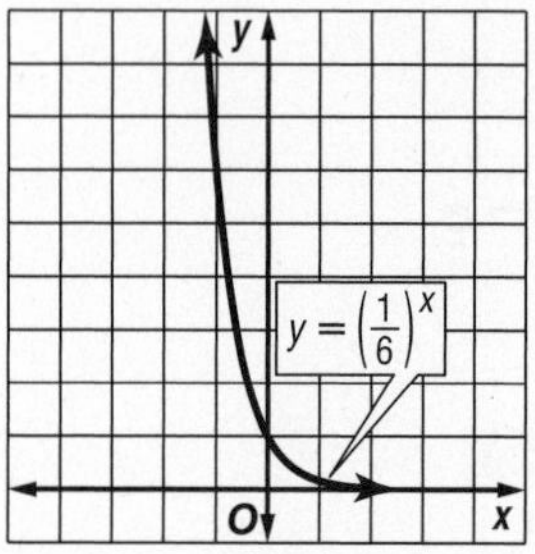

19. 1
3.5

20. No; the domain values are at regular intervals, but the range values have a common difference 3.

21. Yes; the domain values are at regular intervals and the range values have a common factor 2.

22. about \$5030.49

23. about \$4595.27

24. 5184

25. 45 or −45

B: $\frac{1}{2}$

Chapter 10 Assessment Answer Key

Form 3
Page 631

1. 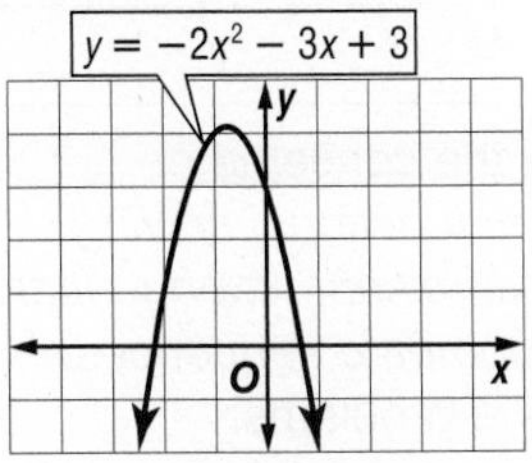

2. 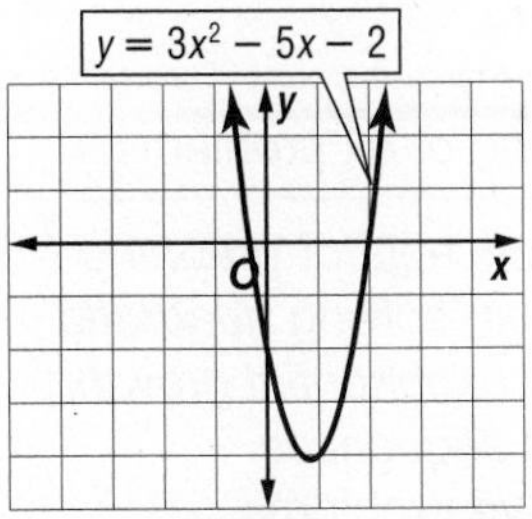

3. $x = \frac{5}{2}; \left(\frac{5}{2}, -\frac{109}{4}\right);$ minimum

4. $-4, 2$

5. $1 < x < 2,\ 4 < x < 5$

6. $-2 < m < -1,\ 1 < m < 2$

7. $-24, -2$

8. 10.3, 23.7

9. $-0.6, 2.9$

10. $-5 \pm \sqrt{25 - c}$

11. $-\frac{2}{3}, \frac{5}{7}$ or $-0.7, 0.7$

Page 632

12. 0 times

13. -18 or 18

14. 4

15. 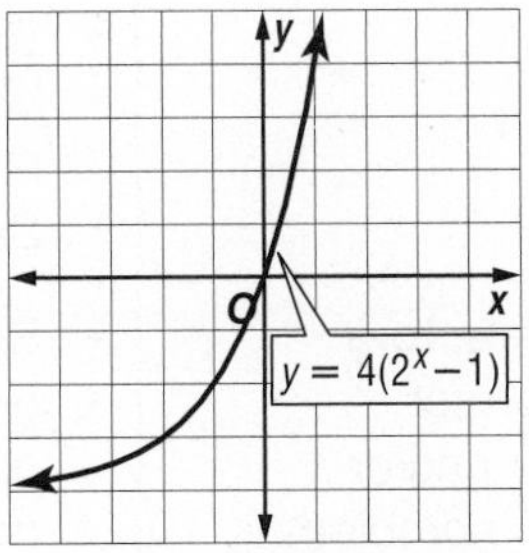

0

16. Yes; the domain values are at regular intervals and the range values have a common ratio 2.

17. about \$112,206.07

18. yes

19. $\frac{14}{81}, \frac{28}{243}, \frac{56}{729}$

20. 48 or -48, 108 or -108

B: $\frac{-7 \pm \sqrt{49 + 16a}}{2a}$

Answers

Chapter 10 Assessment Answer Key

Page 633, Open-Ended Assessment
Scoring Rubric

Score	General Description	Specific Criteria
4	**Superior** A correct solution that is supported by well-developed, accurate explanations	• Shows thorough understanding of the concepts of *graphing quadratic and exponential functions, solving quadratic equations, using the discriminant, exponential growth, exponential decay,* and *geometric sequences.* • Uses appropriate strategies to solve problems. • Computations are correct. • Written explanations are exemplary. • Graphs are accurate and appropriate. • Goes beyond requirements of some or all problems.
3	**Satisfactory** A generally correct solution, but may contain minor flaws in reasoning or computation	• Shows an understanding of the concepts of *graphing quadratic and exponential functions, solving quadratic equations, using the discriminant, exponential growth, exponential decay,* and *geometric sequences.* • Uses appropriate strategies to solve problems. • Computations are mostly correct. • Written explanations are effective. • Graphs are mostly accurate and appropriate. • Satisfies all requirements of problems.
2	**Nearly Satisfactory** A partially correct interpretation and/or solution to the problem	• Shows an understanding of most of the concepts of *graphing quadratic and exponential functions, solving quadratic equations, using the discriminant, exponential growth, exponential decay,* and *geometric sequences.* • May not use appropriate strategies to solve problems. • Computations are mostly correct. • Written explanations are satisfactory. • Graphs are mostly accurate. • Satisfies the requirements of most of the problems.
1	**Nearly Unsatisfactory** A correct solution with no supporting evidence or explanation	• Final computation is correct. • No written explanations or work is shown to substantiate the final computation. • Graphs may be accurate but lack detail or explanation. • Satisfies minimal requirements of some of the problems.
0	**Unsatisfactory** An incorrect solution indicating no mathematical understanding of the concept or task, or no solution is given	• Shows little or no understanding of most of the concepts of *graphing quadratic and exponential functions, solving quadratic equations, using the discriminant, exponential growth, exponential decay,* and *geometric sequences.* • Does not use appropriate strategies to solve problems. • Computations are incorrect. • Written explanations are unsatisfactory. • Graphs are inaccurate or inappropriate. • Does not satisfy requirements of problems. • No answer may be given.

Chapter 10 Assessment Answer Key

Page 633, Open-Ended Assessment
Sample Answers

In addition to the scoring rubric found on page A28, the following sample answers may be used as guidance in evaluating open-ended assessment items.

1. Sample answer: $f(x) = x^2$; $f(x) = 2^x$

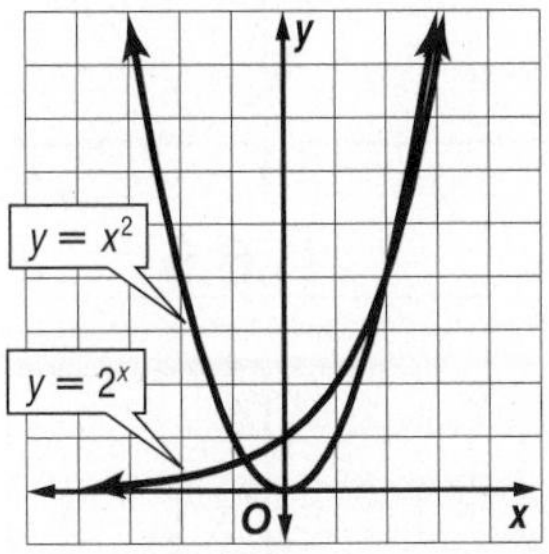

The domains of the two functions are the same, all real numbers. The range of $f(x) = x^2$ is $y \geq 0$, while the range of $f(x) = 2^x$ is $y > 0$.
The quadratic function has a vertical line of symmetry, $x = 0$, and is symmetrical about that line. However, the exponential function has no symmetry.

2a. Sample answer: $x^2 + x + 1 = 0$; -3; The student should explain that the discriminant is the expression under the radical sign in the Quadratic Formula. Since there is no real square root of a negative number, there are no real roots of an equation whose discriminant is negative.

2b. Sample answer: $x^2 + 2x + 1 = 0$; 0; The student should explain that zero has only one square root. Thus, when the determinant is zero the Quadratic Formula yields only one value when you simplify the numerator of the formula.

2c. Sample answer: $x^2 + x - 1 = 0$; Since this quadratic equation does not factor and the roots are not integers, completing the square would be the better method to use to solve the equation.

3a. Sample answer: 5%; about 14.2 years

3b. Sample answer: 10%; about 6.6 years

3c. Sample answer: about 10.4 years; about \$8320

4a. Sample answer: $f(x) = 2(3^x)$;
$f(-1) = \frac{2}{3}$, $f(0) = 2$, $f(1) = 6$, $f(2) = 18$, $f(3) = 54$, $f(4) = 162$; Yes, in this sequence, each term can be found by multiplying 3 times the previous term.

4b. Sample answer: 3, 15, 75, 375, …; The equation $y = 3 \cdot b^x$ can be used to generate this geometric sequence by letting $b = 5$ and evaluating $3 \cdot 5^x$ for integer values of x greater than or equal to zero.

4c. The exponential growth equation $y = C(1 + r)^t$ and the exponential decay equation $A = C(1 - r)^t$ can both be used to generate geometric sequences. In both cases a geometric sequence is created by keeping the values for C and r constant and evaluating the right-hand side of the equations with values for t chosen at regular intervals.

Chapter 10 Assessment Answer Key

Vocabulary Test/Review
Page 634

1. false; zeros
2. false; parabola
3. true
4. true
5. false; common ratio
6. true
7. false; compound interest
8. false; quadratic function
9. true
10. false; exponential function
11. Sample answer: The axis of symmetry of a parabola is the line that divides a parabola into two matching halves.
12. Sample answer: Geometric means are missing term(s) between two nonconsecutive terms in a geometric sequence.

Quiz (Lessons 10–1 and 10–2)
Page 635

1.

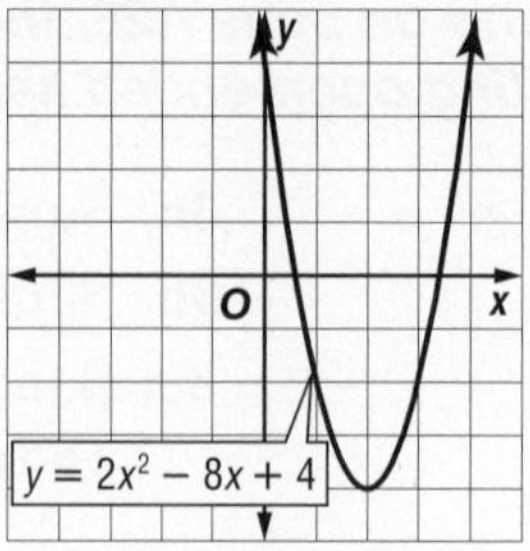

2.

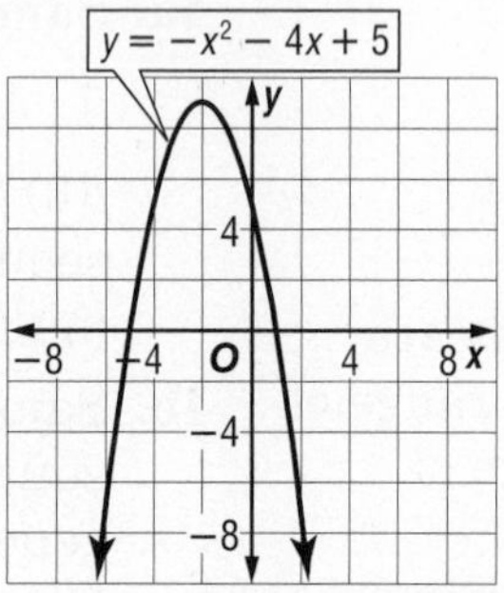

$x = -2$; $(-2, 9)$; maximum

3. C
4. −4, 6
5. $0 < m < 1$, $1 < m < 2$

Quiz (Lessons 10–3 and 10–4)
Page 635

1. 1.5, 8.5
2. $\frac{81}{4}$
3. 2, −10
4. $-1, \frac{7}{4}$
5. −167; no real roots

Quiz (Lessons 10–5 and 10–6)
Page 636

1.

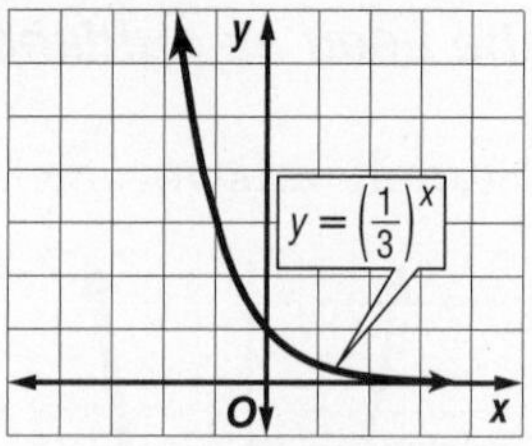

1; 6.5

2.

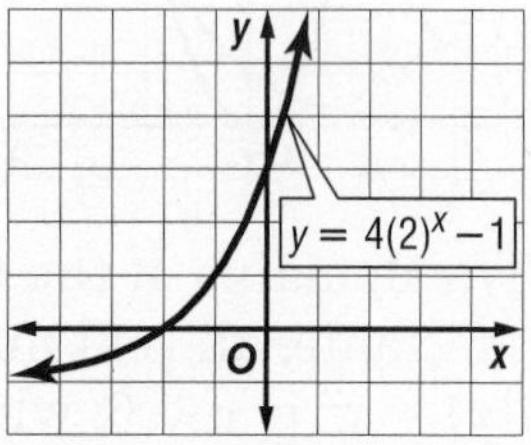

3

3. No; the domain values are at regular intervals, but the range values have a common difference 2.
4. \$2675.04
5. \$19,524.63

Quiz (Lesson 10–7)
Page 636

1. no
2. yes
3. 24, 6, 1.5
4. −1215
5. 32 or −32

Chapter 10 Assessment Answer Key

Mid-Chapter Test
Page 637

1. D
2. A
3. B
4. C
5. B
6. A
7. $\varnothing$
8. $-1, 8$
9. $0 < x < 1, 1$
10. $0 < x < 1,$ $4 < x < 5$
11. $-5.2, 1.7$
12. $\varnothing$

Cumulative Review
Page 638

1. 25
2. 2.5; −5
3. $y = \frac{5}{6}x$
4. $\{y \mid y \geq 5\}$
5. 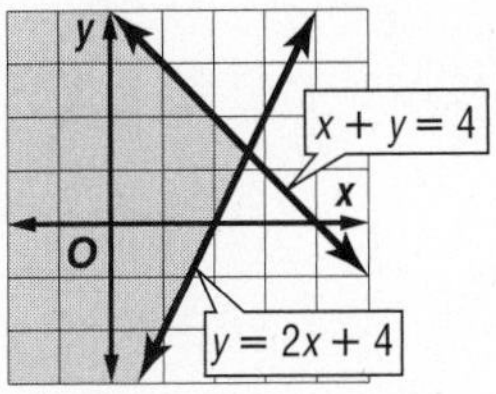

6. $3x^3 + 2x^2 + 4x - 3$
7. $-4x^2y + 9xy - 8y^2$
8. $9a^4 - 4$
9. $(x + 7)(x + 5)$
10. $(2m + 5)(m + 3)$
11. $\{\pm 12\}$
12. 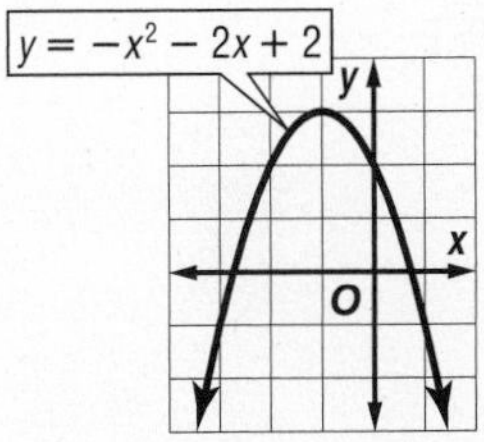

13. 10 s and about 5.6 s
14. about 9,209,514 people

Answers

Chapter 10 Assessment Answer Key

Standardized Test Practice

Page 639

1. A **B** C D

2. **E** F G H

3. **A** B C D

4. E F **G** H

5. A B C **D**

6. E F **G** H

7. A B **C** D

8. E **F** G H

9. A B C **D**

10. E F G **H**

Page 640

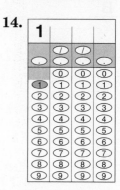

11. 9.8

12. 5

13. 2840

14. 1

15. A **B** C D

16. **A** B C D

17. **A** B C D

Chapter 10 Assessment Answer Key

Unit 3 Test

Page 641

1. $20x^4y^6$

2. $512x^{18}y^{18}$

3. $\frac{b^6}{144g^6}$

4. 3.1×10^{-6}; 0.0000031

5. 3

6. $3a + 2b - 4c$

7. 2

8. $p^2 + 2p - 15$

9. $a^3 - a^2 - 13a - 14$

10. $25t^2 + 10ts + s^2$

11. $9k^2 - 1$

12. $30mnp^2$

13. $4pq(p - 4 + 2q)$

14. $(m - 2)(m - 9)$

15. $(3a - 4)(a - 3)$

16. $3(3r - 2s)(3r + 2s)$

17. $2p - 1$

Page 642

18. $\left\{-\frac{1}{2}, 0\right\}$

19. $\{4, 9\}$

20. $\left\{-\frac{2}{5}, 7\right\}$

21. $\left\{-\frac{1}{2}, 0, \frac{1}{2}\right\}$

22. $\{-9\}$

23. $x = -4$; $(-4, -4)$

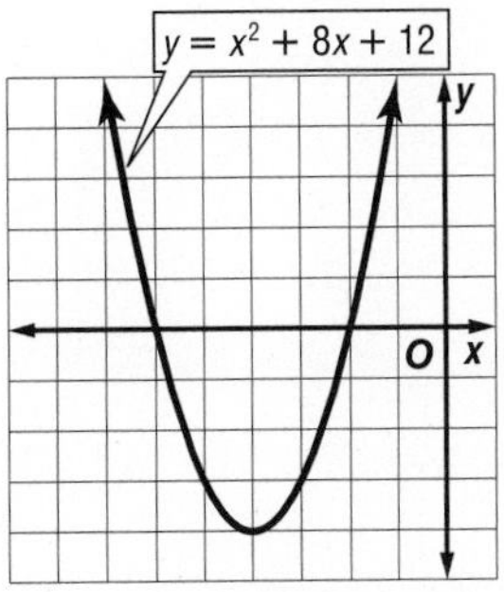

24. $\varnothing$

25. $\{-6, 8\}$

26. $\{-1.8, 1.1\}$

27. No; the domain intervals are at regular intervals and the range values have a common difference 2.

28. about 850,966 people

29. about \$61,032

30. 18, 6, 2

Answers